# FAMILIAR TREES
# OF AMERICA

# FAMILIAR

# TREES
# OF AMERICA

## by WILLIAM C. GRIMM

Harper & Row, Publishers
New York, Evanston, and London

To my friend of many years
JOSEPH A. BRUNTON, JR.,
Chief Scout Executive of the Boy Scouts of America

# CONTENTS

# PREFACE

Nowhere in the world are the forests more diverse—nor originally were they more magnificent—than on the North American continent. Their diversity is due to great differences in topography, in climate, and in soils; but these very differences have made some parts of the continent treeless, or at best but sparsely wooded. In the far north is a treeless tundra where the ground thaws a mere few inches in depth during the brief summer season. There are other vast areas—the prairies and the deserts—where the annual rainfall is far too scant to support the growth of trees.

South of the arctic "tree line" lies a great expanse of northern forest made up chiefly of cone-bearing trees, and it extends southward along the high mountains in both the East and the West. There are "tree lines," too, in many of the higher mountains—particularly in the West—above which trees are not able to grow. In southern Florida, in the Rio Grande Valley, and from southern California southward, the warm climate is conducive to the abundance of tropical trees that grow in their forests. Most of the eastern United States was once covered with extensive forests of deciduous broad-leaved trees, much of which still make the region famous for its brilliant autumn colors. Bordering on the Pacific, from Alaska southward into northern California, are great forests of cone-bearing trees—one of the finest forest areas to be found anywhere in the world.

More than 900 species and varieties of trees have been recorded in North America, north of the Mexican boundary; and should all of the known hybrids be included, the total number would well exceed a thousand. That is more than four times the number of tree species and varieties occurring on the continent of Europe. In just one small area of eastern America—the Great Smoky Mountains National Park—there are almost as many kinds of trees as there are in all of Europe. Many woody plants attain the stature of a tree in one part of their range while elsewhere they are generally thought of as being shrubs. Such is the case with a number of the species which are counted among our North American trees. After all there is really no clear-cut distinction between what we call shrubs and what we call trees. It is sometimes difficult to place a given species definitely in one group or another.

*Familiar Trees of America* is merely an introduction to the many kinds of trees found in North America. It has been possible to include only some out-standing representatives—the more common and familiar trees from various parts of the continent—and to tell the reader some of the interesting facts about them. Most of our states have now adopted state trees. Such trees should certainly be familiar, at least to the residents of these states, and they have all been included in this book. Those who desire to become acquainted with all of the trees growing in their state or region will naturally want to acquire one or more tree identification manuals. A number of these are listed in the appendix.

Much of the information used in writing this book was gathered from the publications of the Forest Service, United States Department of Agriculture; the National Park Service, United States Department of the Interior; and from publications issued by many of the states. Most of the maps showing the ranges of the trees have been furnished by the Forest Service and are reproduced from *Silvics of Forest Trees of the United States* published as Agricultural Handbook No. 271 of the United States Department of Agriculture. Records of the champion trees were taken from the list compiled by the American Forestry Association. This list is constantly kept up to date as new champions are discovered and reported by observers throughout the country. Should you happen to find a tree which you think might become a new champion, take its measurements—height, limb spread, and the circumference of the trunk at 4½ feet above the ground—and send them to: The American Forestry Association, 919 17th Street, N.W., Washington, D.C. 20006.

I take this opportunity to thank Kenneth B. Pomeroy, Chief Forester of the American Forestry Association, for kindly checking the list of the trees included in this book, and for his helpful suggestions. To my wife, Ruth Curtis Grimm, fell the task of critically reading the manuscript, for which I am grateful. And to John Macrae, Executive Editor of Harper & Row, I wish to extend sincere thanks for his interest and for making this book possible.

W.C.G.

*Greenville, South Carolina*

# PART ONE
## *Gymnosperms*

The name "gymnosperm" literally means "naked-seeded." Gymnosperms are seed-bearing plants but they lack what may be called true flowers: the ovules, which develop into the seeds, are exposed and are commonly subtended by a scale. To this group or class of the seed-bearing plants belong the important trees that are known as the conifers, or pines.

# PINE FAMILY  *(Conifers)*

❧ SOME two hundred and fifty million years ago, the first conifers—or cone-bearing trees—appeared upon the earth. This was about one hundred million years before the great dinosaurs and the first of the true flowering plants arrived. These ancestors of today's conifers grew to be large trees in what geologists call the Triassic period, and for a long time they dominated the earth's vegetation. One can see the petrified trunks of some of them in Arizona's famous Petrified Forest, now safeguarded in the Petrified Forest National Monument.

Conifers do not have what can really be called flowers or fruits; they simply produce cones made up of scales. These cones, which appear on their branches usually in late winter or early spring, are of two kinds. Those of one kind, which have pollen-bearing stamens on the lower surfaces of the scales, are often numerous, and from them comes a shower of dry and dusty pollen, which looks like powdered sulfur. It often covers everything near the trees with a fine, yellowish dust. After the pollen is shed, the mission of these little cones is fulfilled, and they dry up and drop off the trees.

Cones of another kind, which appear on the same tree and are less numerous, bear ovules on the upper or inner surfaces of their scales. These ovules are not enclosed within a pistil, as they are in true flowers, but simply lie exposed on the surfaces of the cone scales. Winds carry the dusty pollen to them, and after fertilization has taken place, the cones grow larger and the little ovules develop into seeds.

Conifers do not have leaves with broad, flattened blades; their leaves are narrow, flattened, and needlelike, or sometimes merely scalelike or awl-shaped. Most conifers are evergreens, but there are a few that shed their leaves completely in the fall. Often the leaves are retained for no more than a few years, but the foxtail and bristlecone pines of the western United States hold their needles as long as ten to seventeen years before they are shed. Commonly coniferous trees are called softwoods, and the broad-leaved trees are called hardwoods. These terms, however, are apt to be misleading

3

as far as the actual hardness of the wood is concerned. The wood of certain pines is actually much harder than that of many so-called hardwood trees, for example the willows and poplars.

Most of our familiar conifers have a shaftlike trunk that continues to the very top, giving the tree a cone-shaped or pyramidal form. Along the trunk the small side branches radiate like the spokes of a wheel. The distance between one such whorl of branches and the next represents one year's growth in height. At the very tip is a leading shoot, or "leader," which shows the growth made during the present year. One can often tell the age of a young conifer by counting the whorls of branches and adding a year for the leading shoot at the tip.

Botanists formerly classified all of the conifers as members of the pine family, and some still do so. Recently, however, the tendency has been to divide them into four families, as follows:

THE PINE FAMILY (*Pinaceae*) includes the true pines, spruces, firs, hemlocks, and larches. These are trees with needlelike or narrow and flattened leaves; the cones usually bear two seeds with a terminal wing on each flattened cone scale, but are sometimes wingless.

THE BALDCYPRESS FAMILY (*Taxodiaceae*) includes the baldcypresses and the sequoias. They are trees with narrow and flattened or scalelike leaves; the cones are made up of shield-shaped scales bearing seeds with side wings.

THE CYPRESS FAMILY (*Cupressaceae*) includes the true cypresses, arborvitaes, incense cedars, white cedars, and junipers. These are trees with scalelike or both scalelike and awllike leaves; the cones are made up of woody, leathery, or fleshy scales, which may be either flat or scalelike, and bear seeds that have side wings or are wingless.

THE YEW FAMILY (*Taxaceae*) includes the yews and torreyas. They do not have cones but rather a single seed which is partially or completely surrounded by a fleshy portion.

## EASTERN WHITE PINE (*Pinus strobus*)

Extensive forests of Eastern white pine once stretched westward from southeastern Canada and New England, across New York and northern Pennsylvania, to the region around the Great Lakes. In places the tree formed pure stands. In other places it mingled with the eastern hemlock, the red pine, or the spruces and northern hardwoods. It grew in somewhat lesser abundance southward along the Appalachians into northern Georgia.

For almost three centuries this pine reigned as the foremost timber tree. Lord Weymouth introduced it into England about the year 1705, and to this day the English call it the Weymouth pine. Shortly afterward it was taken to Germany, where it became a prized timber tree.

The eastern white pine is the largest of the northeastern cone-bearing trees. It commonly grows from 80 to 100 feet in height, with a trunk from 2 to 3½ feet in diameter; individual trees have been known to attain a height of up to 220 feet and a trunk diameter of 6 feet. When growing in the open, this pine develops a broadly cone-shaped crown, with lateral branches persisting often almost to the ground. In dense stands the tall, straight, shaft-like trunks are free of branches for two-thirds of their length. In the primeval forest many of these pines were devoid of branches for nearly a hundred feet above the ground. A tree in the Brule River State Forest, Wisconsin, 151 feet tall with a trunk 17 feet 11 inches in circumference, is the current American Forestry Association champion.

Eastern white pine has had a wider range of uses than the wood of any other tree. Before the American Revolution, choice pines in the New England forests were blazed with the King's Broad Arrow, as a sign that they were reserved for use as ships' masts by the Royal Navy; but blazed or not, the big pines were appropriated by rebellious colonists for their own use. The moderately soft, even-textured, and straight-grained wood has many excellent qualities and is easily worked. Until the supply began to run short, it was the preferred wood for all construction purposes. It went into houses and barns, covered bridges, furniture, burial boxes, and dozens of other items, including matches. Today the eastern white pine is still an important timber tree, but it is much less widely used simply because there is not enough of it.

Lumbering of white pine in the forests of New England began about the middle of the seventeenth century, and gradually spread westward until the magnificent virgin stands of the tree were exhausted. By the mid-nineteenth century the center of the lumbering industry had moved into Pennsylvania. About 1860 Pennsylvania led all of the states in lumber production, largely because of its great forests of white pine. During this period great rafts of logs were floated down the Allegheny and Susquehanna rivers, some destined for points as far away as New Orleans. By the turn of the twentieth century, the only virgin white pine forest left was in the southern Appalachians.

Today the center of eastern white pine lumbering is back where it first began—in New England, where most of what is now being cut grew up on abandoned farms. Although young pines come up quickly in open places such as old fields, the tree is unable to reproduce itself in the shade of the forest. The virgin white pine forests were made up of trees that were generally of the same age and size. There were no younger white pines beneath them to perpetuate the forest; instead, there were many shade-tolerant hemlocks, beeches, birches, and maples. Thus when the pine forests were cut, they were succeeded by a mixed forest of the latter kinds of trees. What, then, was the origin of the primitive forests dominated by the white pines? The evidence indicates that the pines seeded into vast open areas cleared either by fires or by extensive windthrows.

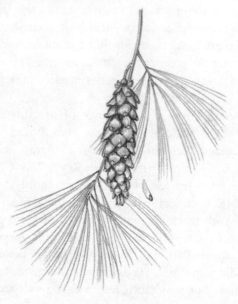

EASTERN WHITE PINE

Eastern white pine grows rapidly once it becomes established. Under favorable conditions, trees may grow from 2 to 4 feet in height, and as much as an inch in diameter, during a single year. Many produce cones when they are no more than 10 feet tall, but good seed production usually does not occur until the trees are from twenty to fifty years old. Growth in height decreases after the trees attain an age of a hundred years; at two hundred years they have about reached their full maturity. Some few eastern white pines, however, have shown rings indicating that they were at least four hundred and fifty years old.

The eastern white pine is readily distinguished because it is the only eastern pine having needles in bundles of five. They are soft and flexible, bluish-green in color, and from 3 to 5 inches long. The spindle-shaped and often slightly curved cones mature in the summer of the second year, and are shed the following autumn or winter. They are from 4 to 8 inches in length; and the thin cone scales are unarmed but often more or less crusted with a whitish, sticky resin.

Aside from its importance as a timber tree, the eastern white pine has several other virtues. It is one of the most beautiful of our native conifers, and several horticultural varieties have been developed. More than any of our other native pines, it has been planted wherever it will grow as a shade or ornamental tree. In earlier days, New Englanders often stripped the needles from the tender young shoots, which they boiled in syrup and ate as a confection. The Indians are said to have eaten the juicy inner bark of the tree, and it is still used occasionally today as an ingredient of cough medi-

EASTERN
WHITE PINE

cines. Maine, Michigan, and Wisconsin all have adopted the eastern white pine as their state tree.

The needles of white pines sometimes show small golden-yellow to reddish-brown spots. A year or two after these appear, blisters develop on the bark of such trees, and exude a yellowish liquid. Still later, pustules containing orange-yellow spores appear on the bark, which dries and cracks, until eventually the tree dies. This disease is the work of the white pine blister rust, a fungus to which all pines having five needles in a cluster are susceptible. Spores from the fungus as it develops on the bark cannot infect other pines directly, but must be carried by the wind to the leaves of currant or gooseberry bushes. There the fungus plants grow until the end of summer, when they produce spores which in turn are able to infect the needles of other pines. Thus the disease can be controlled by eliminating

the alternate host plants of the fungus—currant and gooseberry bushes—
from the vicinity where the white pines grow.

*Pinus* is the classical Latin name for a pine tree and *strobus* is Latin for
"pine cone." Together the two words are the scientific name given by Linnaeus to the eastern white pine.

## WESTERN WHITE PINE (*Pinus monticola*)

This western relative of the eastern white pine grows in the northern
Rocky Mountain and Pacific coast regions, from southeastern Alberta and
southern British Columbia south to central California. In the northern part
of its range it occurs from sea level to about 3,000 feet, and in California it
is found in the mountains between 5,000 and 10,000 feet. It has soft and
flexible bluish-green needles, from 2 to 4 inches in length, which are grouped
in bundles of five. The cones are similar to those of the eastern species, but
are a bit larger, ranging from 5 to about 14 inches in length.

The western white pine attains a height of from 150 to about 200 feet,
with a trunk diameter of from 2½ to 8 feet. A champion recorded by the
American Forestry Association is a tree 219 feet tall, with a trunk circumference of 21 feet 3 inches at 4½ feet above the ground, growing near the
Elk River in Idaho.

The wood of this pine, like that of its eastern relative, is moderately soft,

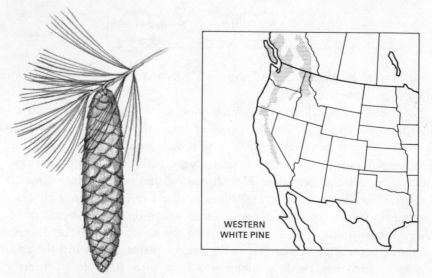

WESTERN WHITE PINE

WESTERN
WHITE PINE

straight-grained, and easily worked. It has, in fact, taken over many of the roles formerly played by the eastern tree. Today it is the wood most often used for making matches, and it supplies lumber for building construction, boxes and crates, and millwork products such as sashes, doors, and frames; and it is often used for making foundry patterns.

Idaho has selected the western white pine as its state tree—and well it might, since about four-fifths of the lumber cut from this tree comes from Idaho; indeed, it is often called the Idaho white pine. Otherwise the lumber comes mostly from Washington, and small amounts are cut in Montana and Oregon.

The scientific name *monticola* means "inhabiting mountains."

## SUGAR PINE (*Pinus lambertiana*)

The sugar pine gets its name from the sweet substance which exudes from wounds in its bark. Its chief distinction, however, is in being the largest of all pines, not only in America but in the world. In addition it has the largest cones (although not the heaviest) among American pines; they range from 10 to 26 inches in length, and from 4 to 5 inches in diameter. Sugar pines are found from the Coast and Cascade mountain ranges of southern

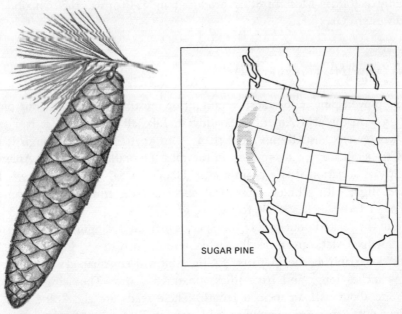

SUGAR PINE

SUGAR PINE

Oregon southward along the Coast ranges and the Sierra Nevada of California. The famous naturalist John Muir called this tree the "Queen of the Sierras." The scientific name *lambertiana* is in honor of Aylmer Bourke Lambert, an English botanist who lived from 1761 to 1842.

The United States Forest Service has a record of a sugar pine that measured 246 feet in height. It stood near the North Fork of the Tuolumne River in California. The American Forestry Association's present champion is one growing on the Stanislaus National Forest, also in California. It has a height of 170 feet and its trunk has a circumference of 31 feet 2 inches at 4½ feet above the ground. In general appearance the sugar pine is similar to the other American white pines.

The sugar pine does not grow in pure stands, but is always found in the company of other conifers. In the southern part of its range it invades the alpine forests and is sometimes found at elevations of 10,000 feet. It reaches its best development, however, on the western slopes of the Sierra Nevada at altitudes between 4,500 and 5,500 feet.

The needles of the sugar pine are 2 to 4 inches in length, spirally twisted, and bluish-green to grayish-green or silvery in color. Like those of the other white pines, they are grouped in bundles of five.

The wood of the sugar pine is similar to that of the other white pines. It is used as lumber for building construction, boxes and crates, millwork, and foundry patterns. Most of it is produced in California, the remainder in southwestern Oregon.


## PINYON PINE (*Pinus edulis*)

The pinyon pine is the most important of the four species of "nut pines" that grow in the arid American Southwest. Like all the others, it is a small and scraggy tree, usually no more than 15 to 30 feet high, although it may grow to heights of 40 to 50 feet on the most favorable sites. The American Forestry Association lists a champion in Utah's La Sal National Forest. It is 33 feet high, with a branch spread of about 43 feet and a trunk circumference of 11 feet 3 inches at 4½ feet above ground.

From the related "nut pines" this species may be distinguished by its stout, smooth-edged, dark-green needles, which are ¾ inch to 1½ inches long, and almost invariably borne in pairs. Its light-brown, egg-shaped cones are 1½ to 2½ inches long, and have thick, unarmed scales. The wingless brown seeds are about half an inch in length. These seeds are the "pine nuts" or "Indian nuts" that are sometimes sold even in Eastern confectionery stores, though they are better known in the Southwest. For centuries the seeds have been a staple food of the Southwestern Indians and Mexicans, but in most other parts of the country they are merely an occasional delicacy. To prevent them from spoiling and to retain their flavor, the seeds are usually roasted as soon as they are gathered. The scientific name, *edulis* ("edible"), refers to the seeds.

PINYON PINE                          SINGLELEAF PINYON

The Pinyon pine occurs in the Rocky Mountain region from southwestern Wyoming, Colorado, and Utah south to western Texas, New Mexico, Arizona, and neighboring Mexico. It is also found in southeastern California and adjacent Baja California. Extremely hardy and drought-resistant, it grows in open stands or scattered groves on the dry foothills, or clings to otherwise desolate slopes and canyon walls. It grows slowly, and some trunks attain a diameter of only a foot in a century or more, but it may live to an age of 375 years.

The Spanish explorer Alvar Núñez Cabeza de Vaca was apparently the first white man to encounter the pinyon, or piñon as it is spelled in Spanish. He and three companions, after being shipwrecked in the Gulf of Mexico in 1528, wandered for eight years through the Southwest before they reached the Spanish settlement in Mexico. Crossing the wide plains of Texas, they came near to dying of hunger; but they happened to stumble into the pinyon country just when the "pine nuts" were ripe, so that Cabeza de Vaca lived to set down the first description of the pinyon pine. Aside from its edible seeds, the tree has very little commercial value. The wood is used occasionally for posts, poles, and mine timbers; and it is good for fuel and for making charcoal. New Mexico has made the pinyon its state tree.

## SINGLELEAF PINYON (*Pinus monophylla*)

Nevada's state tree, the singleleaf pinyon is unique among the world's pines in that the needles are usually borne singly in their sheaths, or very rarely paired. They are pale yellowish-green, 1 to 2 inches long, and usually round in cross-section, and they often persist on the branches for as long as ten years. The scientific name *monophylla* literally means "one leaf." The thin-shelled, wingless seeds are ½ to ¾ inch long, and they have always been a choice food of the Western Indians. In Nevada the Indians still harvest the pine seeds with dancing and feasting, and it is said that much of the bloodshed in early settlement days stemmed from the white man's destruction of these pine trees.

The singleleaf pinyon grows on the dry lower slopes of the mountains and foothills, on the mesas, and in the canyons, chiefly in the Great Basin region from southern Idaho and northern and western Utah to Nevada, in central and southern California, and in northwestern Arizona. It was discovered in 1844 by General John Charles Frémont as he crossed the southern slopes of the Sierra Nevada on the exploring expedition that led to the annexation of California from Mexico.

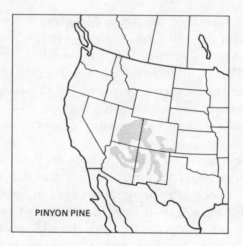

PINYON PINE

## RED PINE (*Pinus resinosa*)

The red pine is distinctly a northern tree, found from Nova Scotia and Newfoundland west to Manitoba and Minnesota, and south through New England to north-central Pennsylvania, Michigan, and Wisconsin. A few scattered trees in the mountains of West Virginia constitute its southernmost limit. Millions of red pine seedlings have been set out in reforestation projects, however, and they are thriving well beyond the tree's original range.

Quite often the red pine flourishes along with the eastern white pine, but it also grows handsomely on sandy soils or gravelly ridges that were too poor to support the white pine. It reached its best development in the upper Great Lakes region, where it sometimes occurred in magnificent pure stands.

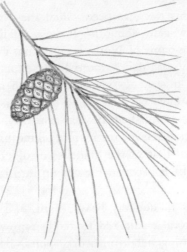

RED PINE

There the trees once attained heights as great as 120 feet, with trunks as much as 5 feet in diameter, though more often they were 50 to 80 feet tall, with trunk diameters of between 2 and 3 feet. A current champion, according to the American Forestry Association, is a tree in Brule River State Forest, Wisconsin. It is 125 feet high and its trunk has a circumference of 8 feet 10 inches at 4½ feet above the ground.

The needles of the red pines are rather slender and flexible, sharply pointed, dark glossy green, and typically grouped in pairs. They measure 4 to 6 inches in length—longer than any other northeastern pine. The nearly stalkless, light-brown cones are egg-shaped when closed but nearly round when open. They are about 2 inches in length and their scales lack prickles.

RED PINE

For many years this tree has been called the Norway pine, but there is nothing at all Norwegian about it. It is a totally American tree. Some believe that it got the name of Norway pine from its former abundance near the town of Norway, Maine. A more likely explanation, however, is that some early explorer mistakenly identified it with a conifer found in Norway, for it seems to have been so called by botanists some years before the town of Norway was established. Be that as it may, the name red pine is far more appropriate. The scientific name *resinosa* means "resinous." The bark of the young trunks, and that of the branches of older trees, is orange-red and flaky. On older trunks it becomes broken up into large, flat, reddish-brown, somewhat scaly plates.

Red pine wood is moderately heavy, hard, and somewhat resinous; the heartwood ranges from a pale red to reddish-brown in color. It goes into building construction, general millwork, poles, boxes, and crates. It was formerly used for the masts of ships, and was often sold along with white pine without any distinction. Aside from its usefulness as a timber tree, the red pine is often planted for shade and ornamental purposes. It is the state tree of Minnesota.

## PITCH PINE (*Pinus rigida*)

No great claim has ever been made for the pitch pine as a timber tree. Sometimes the larger trees are sawed into lumber, but its wood generally finds much more use as fuel than as timber. As a rule it seldom grows to be more than 40 or 50 feet in height, with a trunk from 1 to 2 feet in diameter; but there are occasional exceptions. One growing at the Elkmont Campground in Great Smoky Mountains National Park has a circumference of 9 feet 3 inches at breast height and is about 75 feet tall. The current American Forestry Association champion is a tree at Mays Landing, New Jersey, which is 97 feet tall and is 8 feet 3 inches in circumference at 4½ feet above the ground.

The needles of the pitch pine are stout and stiff, often somewhat twisted, and yellowish-green in color. They are 2½ to about 5 inches long, and always grow in bundles of three. The egg-shaped cones open to become half-round, and they stand at right angles to the branches. They are light brown in color and from 2 to 3½ inches long, and each scale has a small but very sharp and rigid prickle at its thickened tip. The cones usually remain on the branches for many years after they have opened and discharged their seeds. The scientific name *rigida* refers to the rigid cone scales.

The pitch pine grows from Maine and northern New York south along the mountains to eastern Tennessee and northern Georgia. From Virginia northward it often grows along the coast, but generally it is thought of as a tree of the mountain ridges. It does quite well on the most exposed, dry, rocky or sandy soils, but its best growth is on deeper soils with at least a moderate amount of moisture. Among the mountains it commonly associates with various oaks, and with shrubs such as the mountain laurel and blueberry. Occasionally it may even be found in mountain glades where the ground is soaked with water.

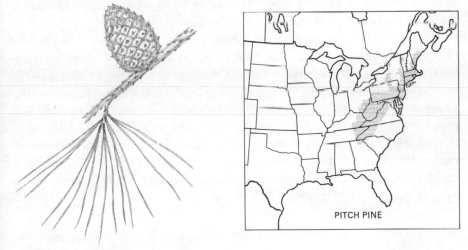

PITCH PINE

PITCH PINE

## LONGLEAF PINE (*Pinus palustris*)

Southward from Virginia's Dismal Swamp is the realm of the longleaf pine. From there on down into Florida, and westward along the Gulf coast into eastern Texas, this pine is seldom long out of sight of the traveler. Its most striking feature is, of course, its tufts of long needles, which are the longest needles of all American pines. They are from 10 to 18 inches in length, quite slender, a shining dark green in color, and arranged in bundles of three. But the cones of the longleaf pine are striking, too. From 6 to about 10 inches in length, and with the shape of an egg, they are the largest cones produced by any of the eastern pines.

The scientific name *palustris* means "growing in marshes," but although the longleaf pine is found throughout sandy flatlands where shallow pools of water often stand in wet weather, it grows best on better-drained sandy soils, and does fairly well even on the drier sandhills. William Bartram in his famous *Travels* made many references to the forests of "lofty pines" he encountered on his journey through the Carolinas, Georgia, and Florida during the latter part of the eighteenth century. There are few places now, however, where even a vestige of those virgin forests can be seen.

The longleaf is one of the most distinctive and important of southern pines. It is often 80 to 120 feet in height, with a trunk from 2 to 2½ feet in diameter, having a long, clear bole and a small, open crown. Larger trees, of course, grew in the primeval forest, up to 150 feet tall, with trunks as much as 4 feet in diameter. A tree 113 feet tall, with a trunk 10 feet 9 inches in circumference at 4½ feet above ground, in Autauga County, Alabama, is the current champion listed by the American Forestry Association.

When seeds of the longleaf pine sprout, they do not grow up immediately into seedling pines as those of other pines do. For several years a young longleaf pine is nothing but a tuft of long needles close to the ground, looking for all the world like some wiry grass. But during this time the young pine is developing a long taproot, which it sends deep into the ground. Then, all of a sudden, it begins to shoot upward as a clublike stem clothed with long needles. Branches come later, but by the time the tree is twenty-five years old it will very likely be about 45 feet tall and have a trunk about 6 inches in diameter. Maturity is reached at about 150 years, and a longleaf pine may live 300 years or more.

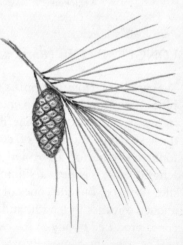

SHORTLEAF PINE

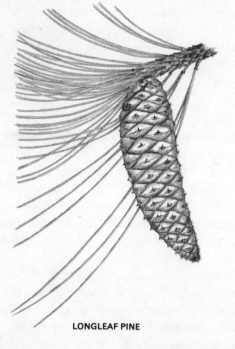

LONGLEAF PINE

The longleaf is one of the South's triple-purpose pines. Its heavy, hard, strong, and resinous wood—along with that of other southern pines—goes to market as "southern yellow pine," and is used extensively for construction purposes, poles, boxes, and crates, among other things. As pulpwood it goes to the kraft paper mills to become wrapping paper, bags, and cartons. The longleaf is also one of the two best producers of naval stores. In many Southern pinelands the trees are "faced," showing long vertical slashes from which the bark has been removed, so that the fragrant, sticky resin can be collected and sent to turpentine stills, where it is processed as rosin and turpentine.

Alabama has made the longleaf pine its state tree.

## SHORTLEAF PINE (*Pinus echinata*)

The dark-bluish-green needles of the shortleaf pine, although shorter than those of other important Southern pines, are longer than the needles of some of the lesser pines with which it commonly associates. Measuring 3 to 5 inches, they grow in bundles of two or sometimes three on the same tree and are slender and flexible. Together with the dull-brown, egg-shaped, and slightly prickly cones—which are only 1½ to 2½ inches long—the needles serve to distinguish this tree from the other southeastern pines. The scientific name *echinata* means "prickly," and refers to the cones. The bark on larger trunks is reddish-brown and is broken into large, flat, irregular, scaly plates.

The shortleaf pine is found from southeastern New York and New Jersey, south central Pennsylvania, southern Ohio and Illinois, and Missouri southward to northern Florida and eastern Texas. Throughout the Southeast it is

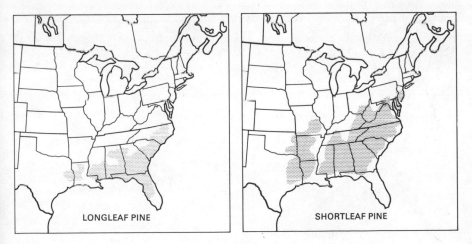

LONGLEAF PINE          SHORTLEAF PINE

an abundant pine on the red clay soils of the piedmont region, and it occurs less commonly in the sandy coastal plain and in the mountains. West of the Mississippi, however, shortleaf and longleaf pines occur in mixed stands and often attain their best development together.

Commonly the shortleaf is a tree from 80 to 100, and sometimes up to 130 feet in height, with a trunk 2, 3, or occasionally even 4 feet in diameter. The current champion, according to the American Forestry Association, is one at Morganton, North Carolina. It is 146 feet tall and its trunk has a breast-high circumference of 10 feet 7 inches. The shortleaf is unusual among pines for its ability to sprout from the stump or when injured by fire, but this characteristic is lost after a tree reaches a diameter of 6 to 8 inches. Maturity comes at about 170 years, and the tree may live to an age of at least 400 years.

The shortleaf is one of the four important timber pines of the South. Its wood, although somewhat lighter and less strong than that of the longleaf pine, is similar, and is sold simply as "southern yellow pine." This is an important pulpwood tree and handsome enough to be planted for ornamental purposes. Arkansas has selected the shortleaf pine as its state tree.

## LOBLOLLY PINE (*Pinus taeda*)

In the Southeast, moist low depressions are locally called "loblollies," and so the pine that often grows in such places received its name. Since it also comes up quickly in abandoned fields, in some places it is called the oldfield pine. From the pine barrens of southern New Jersey south to central Flor-

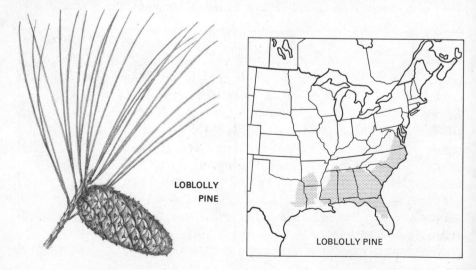

LOBLOLLY
PINE

LOBLOLLY PINE

ida, west to eastern Texas, and thence north in the Mississippi Valley to southern Tennessee, Arkansas, and southeastern Oklahoma, it is one of the commonest of pines. Abundant everywhere in the coastal plain, it ranges inland farther south into the piedmont but with ever-thinning ranks.

The loblolly pine is a large tree, the biggest of all the southern pines. Often 90 to 100 feet tall, it sometimes grows to as much as 150 feet, with a trunk commonly 2 to 3, and occasionally as much as 5 feet in diameter. The current champion recorded by the American Forestry Association—a tree near Ammon, Virginia—has a height of 128 feet and a breast-high trunk circumference of 16 feet 6 inches. Coker and Totten in *Trees of the Southeastern States* reported one in Wilson County, North Carolina, as having a trunk 5 feet 8 inches in diameter at 4 feet above the ground. Still larger trees doubtless occurred in the virgin forests.

The pale-green needles of this pine are 6 to 9 inches long and grow in bundles of three. They are slender but stiff and often somewhat twisted, and have a sharp point at the tip. The reddish-brown and stalkless cones are usually from 3 to 5 inches in length, and the woody scales are tipped with a sharp, stout spine. The reddish-brown bark of the larger trunks becomes deeply fissured into broad, scaly plates.

This is another of the four important timber pines of the South. Its wood, although softer and lighter than that of the longleaf pine, is marketed as "southern yellow pine" lumber, and the loblolly is also a leading pulpwood pine.

The scientific name *taeda* comes from a name given by the ancient Greeks to resinous pines.

## SLASH PINE (*Pinus elliottii*)

The slash pine of the virgin forests grew in low places where there was plenty of moisture, in shallow ponds, and in the branch swamps of the coastal country; it ranged from southeastern South Carolina south into Florida and westward to southeastern Louisiana. Because it grows rapidly, produces good timber, and vies with longleaf pine as a producer of naval stores, it has become a great favorite of foresters, and has been widely planted beyond its original range. It is one of the four commercially important southern pines.

Commonly the slash pine attains a height of 80 to 90 feet, with a trunk diameter of 2 to 3 feet. The present champion of the American Forestry Association is a tree in the Apalachicola National Forest in Florida. It is 119 feet tall with a trunk which measures 10 feet 5 inches in circumference at

4½ feet above the ground. The trunk is often clear of branches 50 to 70 feet above the ground, and is surmounted by a crown of heavy horizontal limbs. During its first twenty to fifty years, the slash pine exceeds all of the other southern pines in growth. In lower South Carolina, seedling trees have grown to heights of 8 or 10 feet in only three years. Trees twenty-five years old have averaged 65 feet in height, with breast-high trunk diameters of

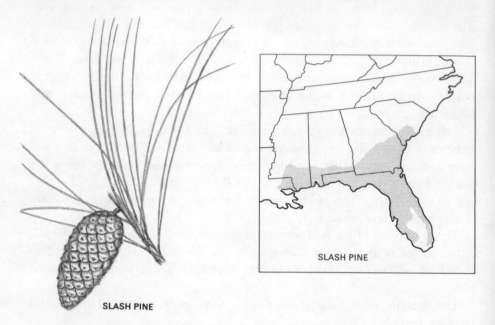

SLASH PINE

SLASH PINE

about 10 inches. Such rapid growth quite naturally pleases foresters and landowners.

The slash pine's dark, glossy, green needles are from 8 to 12 inches long, usually in bundles of two, but quite often in threes, and grow in tufts at the ends of the branches. They persist until the end of the second season. The end buds of the branches are silvery-brown in color, not silvery-white as are those of the longleaf pine. In spring they elongate to form light-grayish "candles" about the thickness of a stout pencil. The stalked, egg-shaped cones are from 3 to 6 inches in length, and so lustrous that they actually appear varnished. Their scales are each tipped with a small, slender, and slightly curved prickle. Old trunks have orange-to-reddish-brown bark, which breaks into large plates covered with thin, papery scales.

The scientific name *elliottii* honors the discoverer of the tree, Stephen Elliott, a noted South Carolina botanist of the late eighteenth and early nineteenth centuries who wrote *Sketch of the Botany of South Carolina and Georgia.*

## PONDEROSA PINE (*Pinus ponderosa*)

Among the trees discovered by the members of the Lewis and Clark expedition when they traveled up the Missouri River in 1804 was a big new pine. Just over two decades later, when the Scottish botanist David Douglas found trees of the same kind growing near the Spokane River in eastern Washington, he was so impressed by their great size that he suggested the name *ponderosa*. For a good many years lumbermen insisted on calling it the western yellow pine, but now the name ponderosa has been officially adopted by the United States Forest Service, and is accepted by the lumber industry.

A ponderosa pine measured by the Forest Service had a height of 232 feet, and others from 150 to 180 feet tall are common. The champion ponderosa pine in the American Forestry Association's register of big trees is one near Lapine, Oregon, 162 feet high with a trunk measuring 27 feet 1 inch in circumference at 4½ feet above ground. Ponderosa pines may live to an age of 500 years or more, and one tree in southwestern Colorado is reported to have had 1,047 annual rings.

Ponderosa pine usually grows in rather open, parklike stands, from the Black Hills of the Dakotas northwestward to British Columbia, and south-

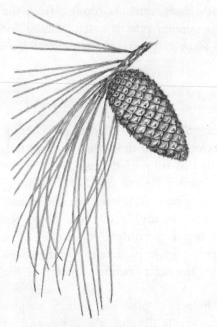

PONDEROSA PINE

PONDEROSA PINE

ward in the Pacific and Rocky Mountain regions to northern Mexico and southern California. Within this range there is considerable variation in the length of needles, size of cones, color of bark, and texture of wood; thus several varieties of the tree are commonly recognized. The trunks of younger trees have a furrowed bark which is brown or blackish; on older trunks the bark becomes yellowish-brown and is broken into large, flat, and scaly plates. The dark-green needles are rather stout, from 5 to 10 inches long, and are in bundles of twos and threes. Normally they remain on the trees from three to seven years. The cones are 3 to 6 inches long, a light reddish-brown in color, and have scales tipped with a slender prickle.

Although botanically the ponderosa pine belongs to the yellow or hard-pine group, its wood is often quite similar to that of the white pines in appearance and properties. Much of it is rather light in weight, moderately soft, and usually straight-grained. It is used mainly for lumber and to a lesser extent for poles, posts, mine timbers, veneer, and railroad ties. The better grades of wood go into sashes and doors, paneling, trim, and built-in cases and cabinets. Poorer grades are used for boxes and crates and the knotty wood is often used as an interior finish.

Commercially this is the most important of all western pines. It ranks second to Douglas fir in the total timber stand in the United States. Major producing areas are in Oregon, Washington, and California. Other important areas are in Idaho and Nevada, with lesser amounts coming from the southern Rocky Mountain region. The ponderosa pine is often planted for shelterbelts in the western states and to some extent as an ornamental tree. It is the state tree of Montana.

## LODGEPOLE PINE (*Pinus contorta*)

The lodgepole pine occurs in two forms. Along the Pacific coast, from Alaska south to California, it is a small tree, seldom more than 30 feet tall, gnarled and with twisted branches. Locally this form of the tree is called the shore pine or the screw pine. The scientific name *contorta,* meaning "twisted," refers to the form of the shore pine. Northward in Alaska and British Columbia it is one of the first trees to invade the peat bogs, but although picturesque, this form of the tree is worthless for timber. The other form of the tree is the true lodgepole pine, a moderate- to large-sized tree of the mountain regions, and perhaps the most common conifer of the Northern Rockies.

Typically the mountain form of the lodgepole pine has a long, slender trunk that is clear of branches for a considerable distance above the ground and a short, narrow, but open crown. Such trees commonly attain a height of

70 to 80 feet, with a trunk diameter of between 15 and 30 inches. Occasionally trees up to 150 feet tall and with trunk diameters of nearly 3 feet have been recorded. According to the American Forestry Association, the present champion is a tree in San Bernardino National Forest, California. It is 110 feet tall and has a trunk measuring 19 feet 8 inches in circumference at 4½ feet above the ground. The name of the pine seems to have been derived from the frequent use of the young pines by the Indians as poles for their lodges or tepees.

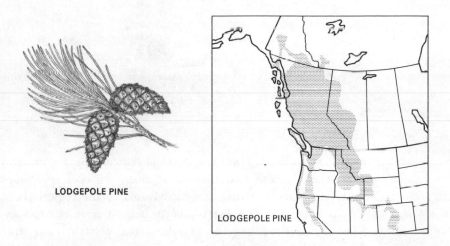

LODGEPOLE PINE

LODGEPOLE PINE

The trunk of the mountain lodgepole has thin, orange-brown to grayish bark with many loose scales. That of the shore pines is reddish-brown to black, and is considerably thicker. But aside from these differences, the two forms are nearly identical. The needles are dark green or yellowish green, often twisted, and from 1 to 3 inches long, and grow in bundles of two. The cones are egg-shaped, often one-sided, light yellow brown in color, ¾ to two inches long, they have prickle-tipped scales.

Lodgepole wood is moderately soft and light, generally straight-grained, and fairly easily worked. It is used for lumber, mine timbers, posts, poles, and railroad ties, and as pulpwood.

## TAMARACK (*Larix laricina*)

In winter a tamarack—like any other larch—looks for all the world like a dead conifer; for larches, though coniferous, shed their leaves completely every fall. Like other larches, too, the tamarack, or American larch, has needlelike leaves spirally arranged on the new shoots of the year; while on growth of the previous season they are densely clustered on short woody spurs. The leaves of the tamarack are a vivid light green, soft, so very slender that they are almost like bristles, and about an inch in length. In fall they turn yellow before they drop from the branchlets. For a short time in the spring the young cones are a bright rosy-red; when they mature in the autumn they are ½ to ¾ of an inch long and light chestnut-brown in color, and they stand erect on the branchlets. Soon their thin scales spread apart, permitting the little winged seeds to be scattered by the winds.

TAMARACK                                    WESTERN LARCH

Tamaracks grow across Canada from the Atlantic coast to the Yukon, and to some extent in Alaska. Southward they occur chiefly in cool sphagnum bogs from New England across northern Pennsylvania to the region about the Great Lakes. At present their most southerly outpost is in the Cranesville Swamp, a boggy area straddling the Maryland and West Virginia state lines; but there is evidence that tamaracks grew much farther south at the time when the northern part of the continent was covered with glacial ice.

Tamaracks typically have a straight cylindrical trunk and an open, pyramid-shaped crown. Uusually they are small to medium-sized trees, seldom more than 40 to 60 feet tall, with trunks from 1 to 2 feet in diameter. They attain their greatest size just north of Lake Winnipeg in Canada, where one occasionally reaches a height of 100 feet, with a trunk up to 2½ feet in diameter. What may well be the largest tamarack within the United States is a tree at Chaplin, Connecticut. It is 60 feet tall and its trunk has a breast-high circumference of 11 feet 5 inches.

Though of relatively minor importance as timber trees, tamaracks occasonally supply some lumber for building purposes, interior finish, cabinet work, and the knees of ships. Because their wood is durable in contact with the soil, they also find use as posts, poles, and railroad ties. The wood is used to some extent in making excelsior.

*Larix* is Latin for "larch." The scientific name *laricina,* meaning "like a larch," was given by early botanists, who placed the tamarack in the genus *Pinus* along with the true pines.

## WESTERN LARCH (*Larix occidentalis*)

The western larch is by far the largest of American larches, and one of the most important timber trees of the Pacific Northwest, where it occurs from southern British Columbia southward into Oregon and Idaho. It is a big tree, often 140 to 180 feet tall, with a trunk 3 or 4 feet in diameter. The largest specimens may exceed 200 feet in height, and have trunks up to 8 feet in diameter. The current champion recorded by the American Forestry Association is a tree near the Kootenai National Forest of Montana, which has a height of 120 feet and a breast-high circumference of 24 feet. Nearly pure open stands of the tree are found in northwestern Montana, northern Idaho, and northeastern Washington, but in most places it is associated with other conifers.

The western larch has lustrous light-green needles varying from 1 to 1¼ inches long. In characteristic larch fashion, they are scattered singly on the new shoots of the year, but are grouped in dense clusters on short spurs along the older parts of the branchlets; and they are shed completely every fall. The upright cones are 1 to 1½ inches long, purplish-red to reddish-brown, and like the cones of the Douglas fir, they have bracts that extend well beyond the cone scales. The bracts of the western larch cones, however, have but a solitary taillike point at the tip.

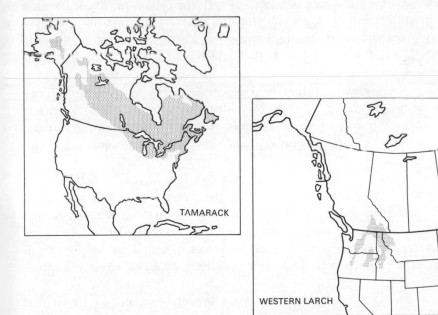

TAMARACK

WESTERN LARCH

The wood of the western larch is moderately heavy, hard, strong, and usually straight-grained. Much of it is used as lumber for building construction, interior finish, and millwork. It is also used for piling, posts and poles, mine timbers, and railroad ties.

Although the tree was reported by the Lewis and Clark expedition and was described by David Douglas in 1826, it was never officially listed until Thomas Nuttall published his *North American Sylva* in 1849. The scientific name *occidentalis* means "western."

## RED SPRUCE (*Picea rubens*)

The red spruce is the common spruce of New England, the Adirondacks, and the Appalachian Mountains; and it is familiar to many as a Christmas tree. In Maine and adjacent portions of Canada it is found along the rocky coast; but southward, in the Appalachians, spruce forests are generally at altitudes above 4,000 feet, where the climate is very much like that of northern New England or southeastern Canada. A New Englander in the forests of the high southern mountains would discover that not only the climate and the trees, but also many of the shrubs and wild flowers, and even the birds and mammals, are the same. Indeed, these high mountains are in what biologists call the Canadian Zone.

Commonly the red spruce is associated with the balsam fir, making with it what naturalists and foresters call the spruce-fir forest—one that can exist only in a cool and moist climate. During the Ice Age, when most of northern North America was deeply buried under glacial ice, a climate suitable for spruces and firs prevailed over most of our Southeastern states, even including the northern portion of Florida. Scientists have uncovered evidence for this, chiefly in the form of pollen grains deeply buried in ancient bogs. Today this type of forest extends only as far south as the Tanasee Bald, on the Blue Ridge Parkway, about eight miles northwest of Brevard, North Carolina.

Ordinarily the red spruce is a tree 60 to 70 feet in height, with a trunk from 1 to 2 feet in diameter, but trees in the virgin forest often grew much larger. According to the American Forestry Association, the largest red spruce on record is 106 feet tall and has a trunk measuring 13 feet 10 inches in diameter at 4½ feet above ground. It grows in the Great Smoky Mountains National Park; where the largest remaining stands of virgin red spruce may be found.

In the open the red spruce develops a broadly cone-shaped crown that extends almost to the ground; but in the forest it develops a long, shaftlike trunk that is free of branches to a height of many feet. The tree may attain an age of between 200 and 400 years.

The needlelike leaves of the red spruce are a dark yellowish-green, pointed and four-sided; and they measure from ½ to about ⅝ of an inch long. Like those of other spruces, they are stiff and are attached to little peglike stalks that remain on the branchlets after the needles fall. When crushed they give off a pleasant, spicy odor. The pendant cones are a light reddish-brown, from 1¼ to about 2 inches long, and have rounded scales with rather smooth edges. Small conelike "flowers" appear in May or June, and the cones mature in the fall of the first year, but they often linger on the branches until the following spring.

Spruce wood is light in color, moderately light in weight, and fairly strong, tough, and hard. It is easily worked and is used for general millwork, boxes and crates, ladder rails, sounding boards for pianos, and parts of violins. It is also much in demand as pulpwood for making paper.

The scientific name *Picea,* meaning "pitch pine," is derived from the Latin for "pitch," and *rubens* is a Latin word meaning "reddish."

## BLACK SPRUCE (*Picea mariana*)

Along with the white spruce and the tamarack, the black spruce is found as far north as trees can possibly grow. From the Atlantic coast of Canada it ranges across the continent to northwestern Alaska. It occurs only as far south as northern New Jersey, northern Pennsylvania, southeastern Michigan, central Minnesota, southern Manitoba, and central British Columbia. Although *mariana* means "of Maryland," there seems to be no evidence that the black spruce was actually ever found there in recent times. In the southern part of its range it is usually restricted to cool sphagnum bogs. It is a pioneer tree on the floating mats which gradually creep outward from the shores of small ponds that are on their way to becoming bogs or "muskegs" through the deposition of plant material. Thus it is known in many places as the bog spruce or swamp spruce.

In such bogs and near the northern timberline, as well as in the rocky uplands, the tree grows very slowly and is often stunted. Robert Marshall once found a dwarfed black spruce near timberline in the interior of Alaska which was only an inch in diameter at its base, though when he counted the annual rings he found that it was 128 years old. In favorable situations, however, it quite commonly becomes a slender, spirelike tree 30 to 50, or occasionally 100 feet tall, with a straight trunk from 1 to, rarely, 3 feet in diameter. The champion, according to the American Forestry Association, is a tree in Superior National Forest, Wisconsin. It is 75 feet tall with a trunk 11 feet 9 inches in circumference at 4½ feet above the ground.

The black spruce has four-sided, blunt-pointed, bluish-green needles from ¼ to ½ inch long, and brownish, downy twigs. Its dull-brown, egg-shaped cones measure from ½ to 1½ inches in length, and they sometimes remain on the trees for twenty or thirty years. Many people are familiar with black spruces as little Christmas trees sold in metal holders containing a liquid to preserve their freshness and usually dyed a deeper green, silvered, or coated with an artificial snow.

Aside from its use as a Christmas tree, the black spruce serves principally as pulpwood. It is ideal for this purpose because the long, white fibers of the wood need little or no bleaching. Sometimes the wood is used for ladder rails, oars, canoe paddles, piano sounding boards, boxes, and crates.

## WHITE SPRUCE (*Picea glauca*)

The white spruce grows across Canada from Labrador to Alaska, and as far north as trees can possibly grow; but southward it crosses the border only in the Northeastern states, northern New York, Michigan, Wisconsin, Minnesota, and Montana. It also appears in the Black Hills. With the possible exception of the black spruce, it has a wider distribution than any of the seven other American species of spruce.

Commonly the white spruce is a tree from 40 to 70 feet in height, with a trunk from 1 to 2 feet in diameter; but occasionally it becomes as much as 120 feet tall, with a trunk diameter up to 4 feet. It attains its greatest size in British Columbia and Alberta, and in the extreme northern part of its range even very old trees may be dwarfs merely a few feet in height. The champion according to the American Forestry Association is a tree in the Superior National Forest, Wisconsin. It is 116 feet tall and has a trunk 10 feet 6 inches in circumference at 4½ feet above the ground.

The stiff, four-sided needles of the white spruce are ⅓ to ¾ of an inch long. They are pointed at the tip, bluish-green in color, and often whitened with a bloom, to which the scientific name *glauca* refers. When crushed the needles emit a strong odor, which some people consider offensive; hence it is sometimes called cat spruce or even skunk spruce. Rather conspicuous stamen-bearing "flowers" appear in May or June, and by fall the lustrous, light-brown, slender cones are mature. They are from 1½ to 2 inches long, and the thin, rounded cone scales have smooth margins.

Open-grown white spruces develop a beautiful pyramidlike crown, and are often planted as ornamental trees. The Black Hills spruce, which most

**BLACK SPRUCE**

BLACK
SPRUCE

**RED SPRUCE**

RED SPRUCE

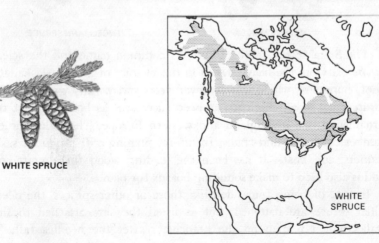

**WHITE SPRUCE**

WHITE
SPRUCE

nurseries list in their catalogs, is now considered to be a variety of the white spruce. This variety is South Dakota's state tree. In Canada the white spruce is an important timber tree and is also used extensively as pulp for making paper. According to Ernest Thompson Seton, the pliable roots of the tree were used by the Indians for lacing birch-bark canoes and for making woven baskets.

## SITKA SPRUCE (*Picea sitchensis*)

Alaska's state tree, the Sitka spruce, is the largest of all the spruces and one of the most important timber and pulpwood trees of the Pacific Northwest. Although its range extends from Alaska southward into northern California, it attains its greatest size in the coastal forests of Washington and Oregon. There it commonly becomes a tree 180 to 200 feet in height, with a trunk from 3½ to 4½ feet in diameter. Occasional specimens have attained a height of 300 feet and a trunk diameter of up to 16 feet. The current champion listed by the American Forestry Association is 214 feet tall with a breast-high trunk circumference of 41 feet 8 inches, growing in Olympic National Park.

SITKA SPRUCE                    ENGELMANN SPRUCE

The Sitka spruce received both its common name and the scientific name *sitchensis* from the heavy stands in the vicinity of Sitka, Alaska. It requires a cool, humid climate and has never been successfully grown in the Eastern United States, although it has been successful as both a forest tree and an ornamental one in England and western Europe. The Sitka spruce provides lumber for boxes and crates, furniture, planing-mill products, sashes, doors, ladders, and boats. It has been the leading wood for aircraft construction, and is also used to make sounding boards for pianos.

Instead of being four-sided like those of other spruces, the needles of the Sitka spruce are flattened; but as usual they are attached to little woody stalks which remain on the branchlets after the needles fall. The upper surfaces of the needles are a bright yellowish-green; underneath they are bluish-white and coated with a bloom. In length they range from ½ to about 1 inch, and they spread outward from all sides of the branchlets. The cones are 2 to 4 inches long and orange-brown in color; and the stiff, rounded scales are irregularly toothed on the margin.

## ENGLEMANN SPRUCE (*Picea englemanni*)

Englemann spruces raise their slender spires of dark blue-green in the high Rocky Mountains from British Columbia and Alberta south to New Mexico and Arizona. In the northern part of its range the tree may occur at elevations of no more than 1,500 feet, but in the southern Rockies it will be found only between 8,500 and 12,000 feet above sea level. It is typically a mountain tree, becoming stunted at timberline, with a twisted trunk and branches only on the side away from the prevailing winds.

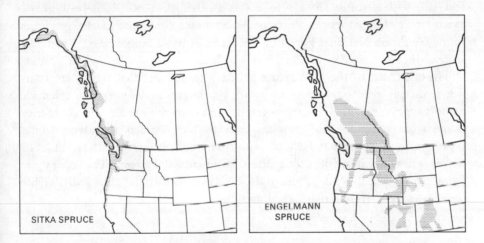

SITKA SPRUCE

ENGELMANN SPRUCE

On more favorable sites the Englemann spruce often becomes a large tree, sometimes as much as 100 to 150 feet in height and occasionally with a trunk as much as 6 feet in diameter. The present champion in the American Forestry Association's roster of big trees is 140 feet tall, with a breast-high circumference of 20 feet 7 inches. It grows in the Williamette National Forest of Oregon.

The Englemann spruce has rather soft and flexible, bluish-green, four-sided needles from ⅝ of an inch to a little more than an inch long. When crushed they emit a strong and rather disagreeable odor. The cones are light-brown, from 1 to 2½ inches long, and the thin cone scales have somewhat ragged edges.

The wood of the tree is used as lumber for building construction, and for boxes, poles, mine timbers, and railroad ties, and as pulpwood. In 1863 this spruce was named in honor of George Englemann, a German-born physician and botanist of St. Louis, who pointed out that it had never previously been described.

## BLUE SPRUCE (*Picea pungens*)

Colorado and Utah have both selected the blue spruce as their state tree; and this spruce of the central Rocky Mountains is known far and wide as one of the handsomest of all conifers. To most people it is familiar as an ornamental tree, for it has been extensively planted both in the United States and in northern Europe because of its attractive pyramidal form and beautiful foliage.

In its native haunts, the blue spruce often becomes a tree from 80 to 100 feet tall, with a trunk from 1 to 2 feet in diameter; occasionally it grows much larger. The American Forestry Association's champion of the species is in the Gunnison National Forest of Colorado. It has a height of 123 feet and a breast-high circumference of 15 feet 8 inches.

The branchlets of the blue spruce bristle with stiff needles, which are four-sided, sharply pointed, and from ¾ to 1¼ inches in length. The scientific name *pungens,* meaning "sharp-pointed," refers to the needles. In color they range from a rather dull grayish-green to bluish-green or silvery-white. Nurserymen have selected those with the most attractive silvery-blue or silvery-white needles for propagation as ornamental trees. The cones are from 2½ to 4 inches long, and light brown in color; the thin and flexible cone scales have irregularly toothed margins.

BLUE SPRUCE

BLUE SPRUCE

The blue spruce—known also as Colorado blue spruce, or simply Colorado spruce—is usually found at elevations of from 6,000 to 8,500 feet in the Western mountains, but may occur at elevations up to nearly 10,000 feet. It seldom forms pure stands, but associates with other conifers. At higher elevations it mingles with the Alpine fir (*Abies lasiocarpa*) and the Englemann spruce. As a timber tree it ranks very low, but its wood is used occasionally for posts and poles, and as fuel.

A common enemy of the blue spruce, and of other western spruces, is a tiny insect, the spruce gall aphid, which causes galls 1 to 2 inches long at the ends of the new shoots. In summer these galls open and release aphids which transfer their attention to nearby Douglas firs. On the latter trees they lay eggs in patches of a waxy white material. The nymphs that hatch from these eggs live on the leaves of the Douglas fir until the following spring. They then lay eggs, some of which hatch into female aphids that fly back to the shoots of the spruces to lay their eggs. For these aphids to complete their life cycle, there must be both spruces and Douglas firs between which they can alternate.

## DOUGLAS FIR (*Pseudotsuga menziesii*)

Today the Douglas fir is the most important timber tree in the United States. It ranks first in the total acreage of timber, first in the production of lumber, and first in the production of veneer for plywood. In size it is exceeded only by the giant sequoia and the redwood. As a shade and ornamental tree it is held in high esteem, and as a Christmas tree it is second only to the balsam fir.

The Douglas fir ranges southward along the Pacific coast from British Columbia to California, and in the Rocky Mountains it is found from British Columbia and Alberta southward into northern Mexico. The very big trees occur in the coastal forests, where they often grow from 200 to 325 feet in height, with great trunks from 6 to 10 feet in diameter. The American Forestry Association's current champion, growing in Olympic National Park, is 221 feet tall with a breast-high circumference of 45 feet 5 inches. The tallest Douglas fir ever known, however, stood near Mineral, Washington. It was approximately 385 feet tall and had a trunk about 15 feet in diameter. Rocky Mountain Douglas firs rarely exceed a height of 130 feet or a trunk diameter of more than 3 feet. Some botanists even insist that they are a different species of tree.

The flattened, narrow, dark-yellowish-green to bluish-green leaves of the Douglas fir are from ¾ to 1¼ inches long. They are slightly pointed at the tip and have a groove on the upper surface. On the underside of each needle is a white band on either side of a prominent midrib. The base of the needle tapers into a short stalk, which is shed along with the needle when it falls, leaving a little oval-shaped scar on the branchlet, as in the true firs. The light-brown cones are from 2 to 4 inches long, and have prominent three-pronged bracts that extend well beyond the rounded cone scales. The cones hang downward from the branchlets in the same way as the cones of the spruces and hemlocks. But the slender, pointed, lustrous, orange-red buds at the tips of its branchlets are quite unlike those of any other conifers.

DOUGLAS FIR

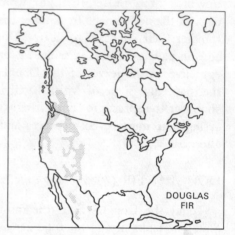

DOUGLAS FIR

This tree has always been somewhat of a botanical puzzle. It is not a true fir, but rather combines the characteristics of the true firs, the spruces, and the hemlocks. For many years it was known by the scientific name of *Pseudotsuga taxifolia,* which translated literally means "a false hemlock with foliage like a yew." It was first discovered by the Scottish physician and naturalist Dr. Archibald Menzies in 1791, on the west coast of Vancouver Island, and the present scientific name is in his honor. The common name of Douglas fir, however, honors another Scot, David Douglas, who spent the years from 1825 to 1834 exploring western North America and collecting plants for the Horticultural Society of England. In 1827, Douglas first introduced the tree into England. There it has since become a popular ornamental conifer.

The Douglas fir is used for building construction as both lumber and plywood. It is also used for sashes and doors, boxes and crates, general millwork, and railroad cars. Smaller amounts are used in flooring, furniture, ship and boat construction, ladders, and tanks. Oregon—whose state tree it is—leads in production, followed by Washington and California. Some lumber comes from other states, among them Idaho and Montana.

## EASTERN HEMLOCK (*Tsuga conadensis*)

Almost everyone will agree that the eastern hemlock—which Pennsylvania has made its state tree—is one of the most attractive of our native trees. Instead of the stiffness characteristic of most conifers, it has a feathery airiness which most conifers lack, its topmost shoot bending gracefully with the wind. Young open-grown hemlocks have a dense, pyramid-shaped crown, with the lower branches often touching the ground. Older trees in the forest develop tall shaftlike trunks which are free of branches to a great distance above the ground and have rather ragged-looking, lofty crowns.

The eastern hemlock is a familiar tree in forests stretching from Nova Scotia and New Brunswick westward through southern Canada to Minnesota and Wisconsin and southward through New England, Pennsylvania, and eastern Ohio, and through the Appalachian region into Georgia and Alabama. Northward it commonly grows on cold, wet soils and on the rocky elevated plateaus; southward it is found mostly on north-facing slopes, in cool ravines, and in the valleys of rushing mountain streams. But the hemlock is familiar, too, as a shade or ornamental tree, and throughout hemlock country is often seen in the form of a handsome, neatly trimmed hedge.

In most places the hemlock grows to a height of from 60 to 80 feet, with a trunk between 2 and 3 feet in diameter. Trees in the virgin forest, however, often reached a height of 160 feet and had trunks 5 or 6 feet in diameter. Most of the really big ones are now gone—except in isolated groves here and there—but in the Great Smoky Mountains National Park a giant eastern hemlock measures 19 feet 10 inches in circumference at $4\frac{1}{2}$ feet above the ground. In the park there are many others which have trunks 15 feet or more in circumference. Foresters tell us that hemlock trees reach maturity at an age of 250 to 300 years, and may live to an age of 600 years or more.

In the days when big white pines were abundant, the hemlock was considered an inferior timber tree. The trunks of big hemlocks in those days were simply felled, stripped of their tannin-rich bark, and left in the woods, where they slowly decayed. Hemlock bark is still in demand at some tanneries, but with a growing scarcity of lumber, the coarse-grained, pale reddish-brown wood of the hemlock—though only moderately strong and hard, and often splintery—has come to be more appreciated. As lumber it is used today for general construction purposes and for making boxes and crates; and quite a bit of hemlock wood goes to the paper mills as pulpwood.

The leaves of the eastern hemlock are soft, flat, and narrow, rounded or slightly notched at the tip, from $\frac{1}{3}$ to $\frac{2}{3}$ of an inch long. The upper surfaces are shiny dark-green, and the lower are marked with two white bands formed by rows of tiny stomata. Each leaf stands on a little peglike stalk that remains on the branchlet after the leaf falls. The leaves are arranged on the branchlets in such a way as to give a feathery appearance. In April or May tiny "flowers" appear on the branchlets, and by October the little, drooping, egg-shaped cones are mature. During the winter the cones shed their little winged seeds, and by early spring most of them will have fallen. Bird watchers know that hemlock woods are a good place to look for wintering flocks of pine siskins, pine grosbeaks, and crossbills.

Hemlock seedlings usually start to grow in the shade of other forest trees, among which they slowly force their way upward into the canopy of leaves and branches overhead. To accomplish this may take a century or more, but in the end the hemlock usually succeeds. Quite often the little hemlocks begin to grow on decaying logs or stumps, and even on moss-covered rocks, eventually straddling them and sending their roots down into the leaf mold and soil of the forest floor.

The scientific name *Tsuga* comes from the Japanese name for the hemlock, and *canadensis* means "of Canada."

**EASTERN HEMLOCK**

**WESTERN HEMLOCK**

## WESTERN HEMLOCK (*Tsuga heterophylla*)

Largest of the four American species of hemlock, the western hemlock grows in the Pacific coast region, from southern Alaska southward a thousand miles or so to northwestern California. It also occurs eastward to the mountains of southeastern British Columbia, western Montana, and northern Idaho. Ordinarily it is a tree from 125 to 175 feet in height, with a trunk between 2 and 4 feet in diameter. Sometimes it attains a height of between 200 and 260 feet, with a great trunk as much as 8 or 9 feet in diameter. The American Forestry Association reports a champion in the Olympic National Park which is 125 feet tall, with a trunk, at breast height, measuring 27 feet 2 inches.

Like the eastern hemlock, the tree has soft, short-stalked, flattened need-les, ¼ to ¾ inch long, dark-green and shiny above, though the two bands of whitish stomata on the lower surfaces are not quite as distinct as those of the eastern tree. The cones are a bit longer, measuring from ¾ to 1 inch, and they have a reddish clay-brown color, but they droop from the tips of the branchlets in the same way. Anyone familiar with the eastern hemlock will have no trouble recognizing its big brother of the West.

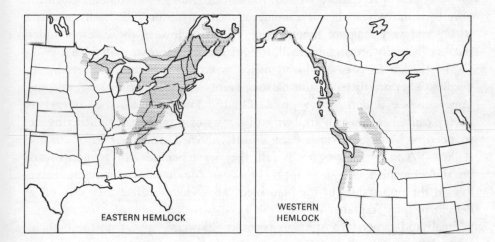

EASTERN HEMLOCK                        WESTERN HEMLOCK

Prior to World War I, little use was made of the wood of the western hemlock except locally. Today it is one of the four major timber trees of the Pacific Northwest. Its wood is heavier, harder, stronger, and less splintery than that of the eastern hemlock. It is widely used for building material, boxes, and crates. In recent years it has also become an important pulpwood tree, and its bark is a rich potential source of tannin.

The scientific name *heterophylla* means "various-leaved." In former times botanists—like many nonbotanists today—considered most conifers to be species of pine. Later, the French botanist Constantine Rafinesque-Schmaltz described this hemlock as one of the firs, but with somewhat different leaves.

## BALSAM FIR (*Abies balsamea*)

Balsam firs raise their dark-green spires in forests across Canada from the Atlantic into the Yukon and British Columbia, and southward into Mary-land and West Virginia, Michigan, Wisconsin, and Minnesota. Typically a tree of cold, moist climates, the balsam fir sometimes occurs in pure stands, and sometimes mixed with spruces or with northern hardwoods. On some bleak, wind-swept mountan peaks it is dwarfed and twisted; elsewhere the trunks are straight and hold aloft a narrowly pyramid-shaped crown that is noticeably symmetrical.

The balsam fir is not a very big tree. Usually it is 40 to 60 feet tall, with a trunk from 1 to 1½ feet in diameter. The current champion in the American Forestry Association's roster of big trees, in Porcupine Mountains State Park, Michigan, is 116 feet tall and has a trunk circumference of 7 feet at 4½ feet above ground. Balsam fir trunks have smooth, greenish-gray bark, on which there are numerous raised blisters filled with a clear, sticky, and very fragrant liquid resin. The bark toward the bases of older trunks eventually breaks into small, irregular, reddish-brown scaly plates.

The balsam fir is easily distinguished from other eastern conifers by its needles. They are flattened and narrow, from ¾ to 1½ inches long, and the upper surface is dark, shiny green. On the lower surface they have two silvery-white bands which are formed by rows of tiny stomata. Their tips are rounded or blunt, sometimes even slightly notched, and their bases are not stalked. When the needles finally fall, they leave behind little roundish scars on the branchlets. On the upper branches the needles commonly curve toward the upper sides of the branchlets, and when crushed they give off a delightful spicy fragrance.

Small and rather inconspicuous conelike "flowers" appear on the branchlets in late spring, and by fall the 2- to 4-inch, purple-tinted cones stand erect like candles among the upper branches. Almost as soon as they mature, however, the cones begin to break up. Cone scales, bracts, and winged seeds flutter to the ground, leaving on the branchlets the spikelike central stalks of the cones. Among our native trees, only the true or balsam firs have cones that disintegrate in such a manner.

A great many people are familiar with the balsam fir as a Christmas tree, and for that purpose the fragrant fir has no superior. Unlike the hemlocks and the spruces, it holds its needles for a very long time after the tree is cut. Balsam fir needles are also a favorite stuffing for pillows. As a timber tree, however, the balsam fir is of no very great importance, though its soft creamy-white to pale-brown wood is excellent for making paper. Liquid resin from the blisters on its bark is known commercially as "Canada balsam," and is widely used for mounting specimens on microscope slides and for fastening together the parts of optical lenses.

The scientific name *Abies,* the classical Latin name of the silver fir of Europe, is now used as the generic name of the true firs. The name *balsamea* is Latin for the balsam tree, and refers to the resin-filled blisters on the bark.

## FRASER FIR (*Abies fraseri*)

The fir of the high mountains of southwestern Virginia, western North Carolina, and eastern Tennessee is a separate species, sometimes called the southern balsam fir but more properly known as the Fraser fir (*Abies fraseri*). It is named for a Scotsman, John Fraser, who first discovered it in the mountains of North Carolina. About the only noticeable difference between it and the balsam fir is in the cones. Those of the Fraser fir have long bracts that project well beyond the ends of the cone scales and bend backward. At elevations between 5,000 and 6,000 feet, the Fraser fir is commonly associated with the red spruce, but above 6,000 feet it often occurs in pure stands. It was the dark forests of these two conifers which gave North Carolina's Black Mountains their name; and the vast stands which once covered the Balsam Mountains suggested the name of that range.

Those who live among the high southern mountains have their own names for the two conifers found there. The Fraser fir is called the "she balsam" because of the resin-filled blisters on its trunk, and the red spruce the "he balsam" because its trunks lack such blisters. The largest Fraser fir in the Great Smoky Mountains National Park—and the record tree of this species—grows about a hundred yards west of the West Peak of Mount LeConte. It is 44 feet tall, and its trunk has a circumference of 7 feet 11 inches at 4½ feet above the ground.

The accidental introduction of the balsam woolly aphid from Europe in 1908 has brought about the destruction of a great many fir trees throughout Canada, the northeastern United States, and the Pacific Northwest. In recent years this pest—which forms extensive cottony-white patches on the trunks and branches of the tree it infects—has killed many of the Fraser firs about Mount Mitchell and along parts of the Blue Ridge Parkway. In August, 1963, it was discovered on Mount Sterling in the Great Smoky Mountains National Park.

## GRAND FIR (*Abies grandis*)

The grand fir—or, as it is often called, the lowland white fir—is the most familiar of the western balsams or true firs, since it occurs from sea level to an altitude of about 7,000 feet. It is found from British Columbia southward to northwestern California and eastward through northern Washington to western Montana, Idaho, and northeastern Oregon.

Standing alone, or in an open forest, a grand fir carries its crown branches to within a few feet of the ground even when it is old. Its crown has the

**BALSAM FIR**

BALSAM FIR

**GRAND FIR**

GRAND FIR

**WHITE FIR**

WHITE FIR

form of a narrow and rather open cone, which is pointed in young trees, but which in old ones becomes somewhat rounded at the top. Downward-sweeping limbs with upturned ends are characteristic. Young trunks have a smooth, grayish-brown bark with resin blisters and blotches of chalky white. On older trunks the bark becomes reddish-brown and deeply furrowed into narrow ridges.

The flattened needles are from 1 to 2 inches long, shiny dark-green above and silvery-white beneath. Their arrangement in two distinct ranks helps to distinguish the grand fir from other native firs. Its cylindrical cones are yellowish-green to greenish-purple, and measure from 2½ to 4½ inches long. Like the cones of all balsam firs, they stand erect on the branchlets and begin to break apart as soon as they are mature.

Grand firs in the coastal forests are often 140 to 160 feet in height with trunks 2 to 4 feet in diameter, and sometimes attain a height of as much as 250 feet with a trunk diameter of 6 feet. Trees in the Rocky Mountains are rarely more than 120 feet tall, with trunks seldom more than 3 feet in diameter. The current champion, according to the American Forestry Association, is 175 feet tall with a trunk measuring 22 feet 4 inches in circumference at 4½ feet above ground. It is in Mount Rainier National Park. The scientific name *grandis* refers to the tree's large size.

The wood of the grand fir is similar to that of the other true firs but has an unpleasant odor when freshly cut. As lumber it is marketed as "white fir," but its chief use is for boxes and crates, and as pulpwood.

## WHITE FIR (*Abies concolor*)

No other western balsam fir has so great a range as the white fir. It is scattered throughout the mountains from western Wyoming and southern Idaho to southern Oregon, and grows southward into Baja California and the southern portions of both Arizona and New Mexico. In the Rockies it occurs at altitudes between 6,000 and 11,000 feet, but elsewhere it is often found below 3,000 feet.

This fir attains its best development in the Pacific region, where it is often 140 to 180 feet high. Heights of as much as 200 feet have been recorded, with trunk diameters of 3 to 4 or, rarely, 6 feet. The present champion white fir, according to the American Forestry Association, is a tree at Mount Diablo Base, Meridian, California, with a height of 179 feet and a breast-high circumference of 27 feet 8 inches.

The massive trunk of the white fir is conspicuously rough, with great, deep, furrows and ridges in its ashy-gray bark, which is thick and very hard and horny. On young trunks and on the younger parts of the older trees, the smooth bark is gray with a brownish tinge, and has conspicuous resin blisters. A dense crown of heavily foliaged short branches, forms an irregular, round-topped cone, which often extends nearly to the ground in old open-grown trees. Younger specimens have beautifully symmetrical distinctly cone-shaped crowns that extend to the ground.

White firs have flattened and usually blunt-pointed leaves from 1 to 3 inches long, silvery-blue to silvery-green in color and arranged spirally on the branchlets. On the lower branches they are often longer than the rest and spread horizontally, while on the upper branchlets they often curve upward. The erect cones are olive-green to purplish, and measure from 3 to 5 inches long.

The wood of the white fir is similar to that of the other balsam firs, and is used for both pulpwood and lumber. The white fir is widely planted as an ornamental tree, and has been grown successfully in the Eastern states, from Virginia north into New England—quite often under the name of silver fir.

The scientific name *concolor* means "of uniform color," and refers to the needles.

## REDWOOD (*Sequoia sempervirens*)

A 385-foot-tall redwood—the world's tallest tree—grows along a tributary of Redwood Creek in Humboldt County, California. It was discovered and measured during the summer of 1966 by Dr. Rudolph W. Becking of Humboldt State College, who was working under a National Science Foundation grant. The tree towers more than 17 feet over the previous "tallest tree" discovered along Redwood Creek in 1963 by Dr. Paul A. Zahl of the National Geographic Society. The new tallest tree has a double trunk measuring approximately 16.8 feet in diameter. The second tallest tree—one 369.2 feet tall—was also found during the summer of 1966. Credit for its discovery and measurement goes to Dr. Paul J. Zinke of the University of California at Berkeley. This tree is in the Founders Grove of Humboldt Redwoods State Park. Many Redwoods exceed a height of 300 feet and are about as tall as an ordinary thirty-story building, with trunk diameters ranging from 12 to about 20 feet.

At one time the "redwood empire" spread over some 2 million acres, all covered with giant trees, forming a belt along the Pacific coast, some 500 miles long but hardly more than 30 miles wide, from extreme southwestern Oregon to what is now the vicinity of San Francisco. The redwoods grew only as far as the fogs rolled inland from the coast, but there they have always been "kings of the forest." To the Indians who lived in their midst, the great redwoods were sacred trees.

Father Juan Crespi seems to have been the first white man to see the majestic redwoods. On October 10, 1769, he made an entry in his journal describing the "very high trees." It was not until 1824, however, that the first really scientific description of the tree was published, giving it the name *Taxodium sempervirens* in the belief that it was one of the bald cypresses. In 1847 the German botanist Stephan Endlicher, concluding that the tree was not a bald cypress, renamed it *Sequoia sempervirens* in honor of Sequoyah, the half-breed Cherokee Indian who invented the alphabet used by his tribe. The name *sempervirens* means "evergreen."

Actually the redwood and the bald cypress of the southeastern swamps are distant cousins. Both have leaves that are narrow, flattened, and arranged on slender branchlets in featherlike, spreading rows. Those of the redwood, however, remain green on the branchlets for three or four years, and then cling for another year or two after dying and turning brown. The leaves on the lateral branches are from ½ to 1 inch long, but those on the tips of the leading shoots and on cone-bearing branchlets are much shorter. They are a dark yellowish-green above and have two white lines on the lower surface.

Like those of the bald cypress, the cones of the redwood have shield-shaped scales. The egg-shaped cones are made up of from fifteen to twenty such scales, each usually bearing five or six minute seeds with pairs of delicate wings. It is difficult to believe that this immense tree could grow from a seed so tiny and light that 8,000 weigh no more than an ounce.

William A. Dayton wrote of the redwood in the October, 1957, issue of the *National Geographic Magazine:*

> In 1948 redwood stands were estimated at scarcely one-third of the original forest. In one year alone, early in this century, 660 million board feet went the way of Walt Whitman's dying redwood, to "the music of choppers' axes, the falling trunk and limbs, the crash, the muffled shriek, the groan . . ."

Today the big old redwoods are still going, but at a still faster rate, to the music of chain saws, draglines, and tractors. Largely through the efforts of the Save-the-Redwoods League, some 50,000 acres of the big redwoods have been set aside in parks and protected groves. The National Park Service has estimated that very few groves of virgin redwoods will remain outside of such parks by the year 2000 if the present rate of cutting continues. *Audubon Magazine* for November-December 1965 contained a photograph of giant logs, many of them 6 feet in diameter, which the previous summer had covered some seven acres at one lumber company's mill. There can be no question that the great virgin redwood forest is going, and going fast.

Conservationists throughout the nation have been advocating the establishment of a Redwoods National Park. After a thorough study, the National Park Service has proposed the boundaries of an area that includes, among others, the grove containing the tallest known tree. Only half of the 53,000 acres recommended for the park contain virgin stands of trees, and loggers are busily cutting many of the groves within the area. Already the grove on Redwood Creek containing some of the world's tallest trees is three-quarters encircled by the aftermath of logging operations. Haste is imperative if the proposed park is to be realized.

Redwoods have a furrowed, fibrous bark from 3 inches to 1 foot thick, which has served to protect them from virtually every enemy but man. Although neither as huge in girth nor as long-lived as the giant sequoia, redwoods have been known to attain an age of at least 2,000 years. The tree puts up a remarkable fight for survival. It will sprout readily from the stump, and the sprouts grow into a circle of young trees. Fallen trunks often send up rows of sprouts which likewise become new trees. According to foresters, the redwood grows so rapidly that on many cut-over areas the sprouts may become trees large enough to be cut again within forty or fifty years. Properly managed, a redwood forest should be able to yield timber indefinitely.

The heartwood of the tree varies from a light cherry to a dark mahogany-red in color, whence the name redwood. It is moderately light, hard, and strong, and is very resistant both to decay and to the attacks of insects such as termites. Most of the lumber produced is used for building purposes: for siding, sashes, doors, and other millwork. Because of its durability it is exceedingly useful for outdoor furniture, cooling towers, tanks and silos, greenhouses, garden trellises, posts, and fencing material. Even the bark makes a very good insulating material.

## GIANT SEQUOIA (*Sequoia gigantea*)

The giant sequoias—or bigtrees, as they are often called—no longer have the distinction of being the world's oldest living things, although they are still unchallenged as the biggest. The oldest known giant sequoias are between 3,000 and 4,000 years old, whereas the age of some of the bristlecone pines in the Inyo National Forest of California has been determined to be in excess of 4,600 years.

Compared with the sequoias, these ancient pines are insignificant trees. The tallest barely reaches a height of 40 feet. Their branches are twisted and often the trees are half dead, and they have very aptly been likened to "living driftwood." They live in one of the most inhospitable and barren environments imaginable, at an altitude of 10,000 feet in the White Mountains, whipped by vicious winds, blasted by sand and sleet, enduring both great extremes of temperature and prolonged drought. Some of them have been able to make less than an inch of growth in a hundred years, yet miraculously they have clung to life through the centuries.

The sequoias (the name *gigantea* means "giant") grow in a narrow belt, 250 miles long, on the western slope of the Sierra Nevada, from Placer County south to southern Tulare County, at elevations between 4,000 and 5,000 feet. Here the climate is cool but not harsh, and precipitation is abundant. The soils are deep sandy or gravelly loams. Snow covers the ground for three to six months of the year, and winter temperatures some-

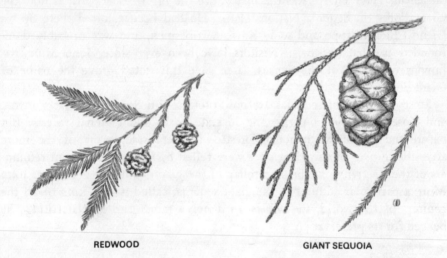

REDWOOD          GIANT SEQUOIA

times drop below zero; but compared with the bleak summits inhabited by the bristlecone pine, the conditions under which the giant sequoias live are moderate.

The largest and most famous of the giant sequoias is the General Sherman Tree in Sequoia National Park. It is 272 feet tall, and the diameter of its trunk at the base is 36½ feet. The largest of its branches is 7 feet in diameter; an average-sized man could lie crosswise on it without being seen from the ground 130 feet below. The mammoth tree was discovered in 1879 by a trapper, James Wolverton, who named it for his commanding officer in the Civil War.

Second in size, and almost equally well known, is the General Grant Tree in Kings Canyon National Park, which adjoins Sequoia National Park on

the north. The patriarch in a grove of giant trees, the General Grant Tree
has become a sort of national Christmas tree. Each year since 1925, a ceremony has been held at its base on the Sunday before Christmas. A choir,
usually chosen from the high school choruses of Fresno County, sings traditional carols, and the speaker is often a guest minister, sometimes from a
distant part of the nation. As a part of the ceremony, a wreath of Christmas
greens is placed on the trunk of the tree by the park superintendent, and
the service always closes as it began, with the sounding of a trumpet in the
grove of the giants.

One of the first white men to see these giant trees was a miner, A. T.
Dodd, who made his discovery while pursuing a grizzly bear, and in his
astonishment let the bear get away. Six years later, in 1858, a pioneer
cattleman, Hale Tharp, was the first to see the big trees of what is now the
Giant Forest in Sequoia National Park. He had been escorted there by his
friend Chief Chappo and some Kaweah tribesmen, and was probably dum-
founded at what he saw, as visitors have been ever since. John Muir, the
famous naturalist of the Sierras, later gave this noted grove the name of
Giant Forest.

Most of the giant sequoias are now protected in Sequoia, Kings Canyon,
and Yosemite national parks, and in state parks and national forests. But
before the parks and national forests were set aside, many of the more
accessible groves of the giant trees were felled by lumbermen. Grim remind-
ers of their activity may be seen today in the giant stumps that remain. John
Muir, a particular admirer of the giant sequoia, called it the "king of all the
conifers of the world, the noblest of a noble race," and in his writings he
begged for its preservation.

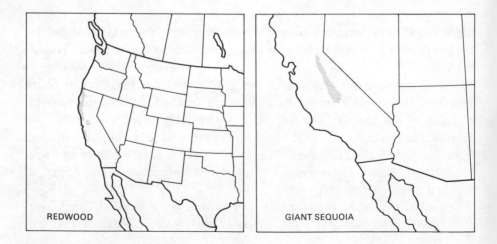

REDWOOD

GIANT SEQUOIA

The giant sequoia does not attain the great height of either the redwood or the Douglas fir, but in trunk diameter and sheer bulk no tree approaches it. The tallest giant sequoias rise close to 300 feet, but more commonly they are from 200 to 280 feet in height. The bigger ones have trunks from 25 to 37 feet in diameter, although a more frequent measurement is from 12 to 18 feet. The sequoias' longevity can be attributed to their thick, asbestoslike bark—which on the older trunks is commonly 1 to 2 feet thick—and to their tannin-laden wood, as well as to their remarkable recuperative powers. They grow new wood over fire scars, and they produce new branches, and even new crowns, to replace those broken by the elements. Even the oldest sequoias retain their vigor and vitality and continue to produce crops of seeds; but unlike the redwoods, they do not sprout from the stump.

For such an immense tree, the leaves of a giant sequoia are remarkably small. They consist of stiff, sharply pointed, deep-green scales from ⅛ to about ¼ inch long on most branches; those on the leading shoots are a little larger. The leaves remain on the branchlets for three or four years. The somewhat barrel-shaped cones are from 2 to a little more than 3 inches long, and each shield-shaped, wrinkled scale usually has from two to nine double-winged seeds, so small that one weighs only .006 ounce. From such tiny seeds grow monarchs which may weigh as much as 6,000 tons. Although the cones mature in the autumn of the second year, they often remain on the branches for as long as twenty years.

Young giant sequoias differ considerably in appearance from the venerable giants, having a cone-shaped crown with branches reaching to the ground. Later the trees broaden out, develop large lateral limbs, and shed their lower branches. In groves of the big trees one will find sequoias at all stages of growth—from tiny seedlings to the great giants.

## BALD CYPRESS (*Taxodium distichum*)

Deep in the heart of a cypress swamp, one has the sensation of being somehow taken back millions of years into the prehistoric past. It is an eerie and yet fascinating place, where the dark water mirrors the trunks of the trees and where long festoons of Spanish moss sway overhead. Even the great saurians of the past appear to linger there in the form of alligators and the odd anhingas, or snakebirds, which look as if they belonged to the time when birds first evolved from their scaly reptilian ancestors. And the bald cypress is, as a matter of fact, one of the last representatives of an ancient race of trees. Many millions of years ago, such trees flourished in forests throughout North America and in northern Europe. Now this tree is one of three remaining species that are a link with a dim and distant past.

Bald cypresses grow in the deep river swamps along the Atlantic coast, from southern Delaware south to Florida, westward along the Gulf coast into southeastern Texas, and northward up the Mississippi Valley to southern Indiana and Illinois. In the virgin forests they once reared their irregular and flattened crowns to heights of 100 to 150 feet from grotesquely swollen bases, above which the trunks were often 5 to 15 feet in diameter. Many of these giant trees were more than a thousand years old. Now, however, most of the virgin swamp forests with their big bald cypresses are gone.

Perhaps the largest of the giant bald cypresses remaining today is the "Sovereign Cypress," in a swamp between Sanford and Longwood, Florida. According to the Florida Forest Service this tree is 125 feet tall, 54 feet in circumference, and estimated at about 3,000 years old. To the south is perhaps the largest stand of virgin bald cypress left today. This remnant of the forest which once covered the Big Cypress Swamp is fortunately preserved in the Corkscrew Swamp Sanctuary of the National Audubon Society.

Although the bald cypress is a conifer, it is not an evergreen, for its leaves—and even the slender little branchlets that bear them—are completely shed each fall. The pale-green leaves are flat and narrow, from ⅜ to ¾ inch long, and are arranged featherlike in two rows on slender branches a few inches in length. In the fall they turn a golden yellow and then bronze before being shed. *Taxodium,* meaning "yew-like," and *distichum,* meaning "two-ranked," both refer to the leaves. The ball-shaped cones are an inch or a little more in diameter. They are made up of several hard, shieldlike scales which fit closely together; and under each scale may be a pair of horny, three-winged seeds. Too heavy to be carried by the winds, the seeds simply drop into the water.

A unique feature of the bald cypress is the "knees," cone-shaped structures that rise out of the water from the tree's submerged roots. These knees are hollow, and it has long been supposed that they furnish air to the roots beneath the swamp water. But their true function is still uncertain, for experiments conducted by the Forest Service have shown that the trees grow just as well without them. The knees are often made into lamp bases and other objects, which natives sell to tourists passing through the cypress country.

The wood of the bald cypress has long been famous for its great durability, and is advertised as "the wood eternal." That durability is beyond question. In the State Museum at the Cabildo in New Orleans there is a piece of water pipe made of cypress wood, still in perfect condition, although it had been buried for over a hundred years. Workmen digging for a subway in Philadelphia once came across the stump of a big bald cypress some 38 feet below the surface of the ground. It too was remarkably well preserved; yet scientists at the Academy of Natural Sciences estimated its age at about 100,000 years.

The moderately hard, strong, and heavy wood is used for many purposes, especially where resistance to decay is required. Among these are coffins, tanks and vats, ships, greenhouses, poles and piling, stadium seats, shingles, siding, boxes, and crates.

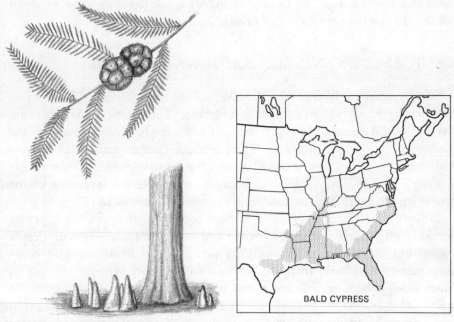

BALD CYPRESS

BALD CYPRESS

## POND CYPRESS (*Taxodium ascendens*)

The edges of pineland ponds in the Southeast are the habitat of another tree, called the pond cypress (*Taxodium ascendens*). Some botanists say that it is merely a variety of the bald cypress, but its leaves are small and scalelike and quite closely pressed against the slender branchlets. The trunks have a much thicker bark, which is soft and shreddy. This species never becomes as large as the bald cypress of the river and tidewater swamps. But both are often planted as ornamental trees, since they do well on higher and drier ground than they usually occupy under natural conditions. In fact, they do very well quite far from their native habitat.

## MONTEZUMA BALD CYPRESS (*Taxodium mucronatum*)

A third species is the Montezuma bald cypress (*Taxodium mucronatum*), which is found from extreme southern and southwestern Texas and northeastern Mexico southward to Guatemala. Unlike the other two, it is an evergreen. One of the world's most famous trees belongs to this species. It is the Cypress of Tule which grows in the churchyard at the Indian village of Santa Maria del Tule, a few miles east of the city of Oaxaca, Mexico. This great tree is about 114 feet in height, and its trunk has a diameter of about 36 feet. Its age has been estimated to be at least 4,000 years.

## CALIFORNIA INCENSE CEDAR (*Librocedrus decurrens*)

Nine species of incense cedars make up the only genus of conifers to encircle the Pacific Ocean in both hemispheres. The North American member of this distinguished group is the California incense cedar, found on the western slopes of the mountains from western Oregon southward to Baja California, and in a few scattered areas of western Nevada. Credit for its discovery goes to General John C. Frémont, who collected specimens of the tree along the South Fork of California's American River in 1844.

Striking characteristics of older incense cedars are their rapidly tapering trunks with widely buttressed bases, and their cinnamon-brown, deeply ridged and furrowed bark. Young trees have a thin, smooth or slightly scaly cinnamon-colored bark. In youth the crown is typically cone-shaped, but in older trees it becomes columnar and irregular and is often deformed by mistletoe and witches' brooms. The leaves consist of dark-yellowish-green scales from ⅛ to ½ inch long, arranged in whorls of four, and closely pressed to the branchlets except at their tips. Each leaf has a long base running down the branchlet. The branchlets form flattened sprays, which give off a pleasing aromatic odor, when crushed. *Librocedrus* comes from two Greek words, meaning "drop" and "cedar."

The drooping cones are another distinctive feature of the California incense cedar. Each one is ¾ to 1½ inches long, and has half a dozen leathery, leaflike scales. Two of these are much larger than the others and cover the cone, so that when partially open it has rather the shape of a duck's bill. By fall the cones mature and open to discharge small, winged, strawberry-colored seeds, which are often so abundant that they form a pink carpet on the ground.

At maturity, incense cedars commonly attain a height of 75 to 110 feet, with a trunk 3 to 4 feet in diameter. Occasionally one is as much as 186 feet tall with a trunk diameter up to 8 feet. The American Forestry Association reports a champion in the Rogue River National Forest of California, which has a trunk circumference of 36 feet at 4½ feet above the ground. Pure stands of the tree are virtually unknown, but in some places it forms up to 50 per cent of the mixed coniferous forest, and it is almost always a companion of the giant sequoia. Incense cedars grow slowly and reach maturity only at about 300 years, but few are likely to live more than 500 years.

The chances are that any pencils you use will be made of incense cedar, which is now the leading pencil wood. Light-weight and soft, it has a spicy fragrance. The heartwood of the tree is light brown, often tinged with red, and the sapwood is cream-colored to white. Aside from pencils it is used for venetian blinds, chests, and toys. Locally it goes into lumber for rough construction. Because it is durable in contact with the soil, the wood often goes into railroad ties and fence posts, and would probably have still wider use were it not for the pecky rot, caused by a fungus, by which it is often disfigured.

## NORTHERN WHITE CEDAR (*Thuja occidentalis*)

Although Americans call a number of native trees "cedars," none of the true cedars grows wild in the New World. True cedars are evergreen trees with stiff, sharp-pointed needles which, like those of the larches, are clustered on short spurs except on the leading shoots, and with barrel-shaped cones which break apart on the trees like those of the balsam firs. One of these true cedars is the biblical cedar of Lebanon (*Cedrus libani*), now a very rare tree. Another is the Deodar cedar (*Cedrus deodara*), a native of the Himalayas, which is commonly planted as an ornamental tree in the Southeastern states and in California.

Another and really much better name for the northern white cedar is eastern arborvitae, as it is called by horticulturists; but since foresters and lumbermen persist in calling it a white cedar, you can take your choice. At any rate, it is a well-known tree, particularly in the northeastern section of the country. It grows from Nova Scotia westward to southern Manitoba, southward chiefly to Connecticut, and westward through the Great Lakes region to northern Minnesota. In the Appalachians there are—or have been—scattered specimens as far south as North Carolina. One tree near Virginia's famous Natural Bridge is 90 feet tall, with a trunk circumference of 5 feet 4½ inches at 4½ feet above the ground, and has been estimated to be more than 1,600 years old.

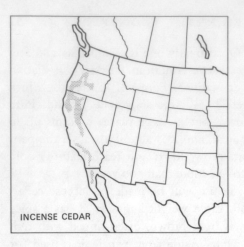

INCENSE CEDAR

INCENSE CEDAR

NORTHERN WHITE CEDAR

NORTHERN WHITE CEDAR

WESTERN
RED CEDAR

WESTERN RED CEDAR

**ATLANTIC WHITE CEDAR**

ATLANTIC WHITE CEDAR

**PORT ORFORD CEDAR**

PORT ORFORD
CEDAR

**EASTERN RED CEDAR**

EASTERN RED CEDAR

More commonly the northern white cedar is a tree 40 to 50 feet tall, with a trunk 2 to 3 feet in diameter, although occasionally it grows much larger. The American Forestry Association's champion is a tree on South Manitou Island, Leelanau County, Michigan, which has a height of 111 feet and a trunk 17 feet 2 inches in circumference. In the north the tree is usually found in cool swamps, along streams, and near lakes, where it sometimes forms almost impenetrable pure stands. In the southernmost part of its range, it invariably occurs on limestone outcrops where gorges have been cut by streams.

The tiny scalelike leaves are arranged on the branchlets in two flattened rows, and the branchlets in turn form fan-like, vertically held sprays. Each little yellowish-green leaf is barely ⅛ inch long and has an almost invisible glandular dot at its center. When bruised, the leaves give off a pleasant tansylike odor. The tiny cones, which mature in late summer, are pale yellowish or reddish-brown, and are from ⅓ to ½ inch long. They have from six to twelve erect, round-topped scales, four of which usually produce tiny, winged light-brown seeds, so small that about 325,000 weigh only a pound.

Friendly Indians gave the members of Jacques Cartier's expedition, who discovered the St. Lawrence River, a tea brewed from branchlets of the northern white cedar as a remedy for scurvy. The tea apparently worked wonders because of the vitamin C contained in the sap, and in gratitude the Frenchmen carried the tree, to which they gave the name of arborvitae, back to France. There it soon found favor as an ornamental, and it is still in favor today both in this country and abroad. Horticulturists have developed many varieties.

The pale-yellowish-brown, aromatic wood, although light in weight and rather soft and brittle, is highly resistant to decay. At one time the tree was of great commercial importance in the Lake States, but most of the profitable stands are now gone. As lumber it has been widely used for boats, tanks, millwork, and boxes. The trunks have provided poles, posts, and railroad ties, buckets, shingles, and net floats for fishermen. An aromatic oil distilled from the leaves and branchlets has been used medicinally.

The scientific name *Thuja* comes from the Greek word for an aromatic wood highly prized in ancient times, and *occidentalis* means "western"— that is, of the Western Hemisphere.

## WESTERN RED CEDAR (*Thuja plicata*)

Scientific names may tell us at a glance the relationships of various plants, but common names are quite often a welter of hopeless confusion. An example is the western red cedar. From its common name one would logically suppose that it is a western relative of the eastern red cedar, but this is not so. Rather, it is a very close relative of the northern white cedar, or another of the arborvitaes. The occasionally used name of giant arborvitae would be much more appropriate.

By far the largest of our two native arborvitaes, the western red cedar was first discovered by the Malaspina expedition on the west side of Vancouver Island, near Nootka Sound, in 1791. Today it is one of the four most important timber trees of the Pacific Northwest. Under favorable conditions it is commonly 150 to 200 feet in height, with a trunk from 4 to 8 feet in diameter. Occasionally it attains a height of 250 feet, and the trunk diameter has been known to reach 18½ feet. The American Forestry Association's current champion is a tree in the Olympic National Park, which is 130 feet tall and has a trunk circumference of 66 feet 1 inch at 4½ feet above ground.

At least it can be said that there is something red about the western red cedar—namely, its stringy, fibrous cinnamon-colored bark. The small, bright-green, scalelike leaves are closely pressed to the branchlets like those of the northern white cedar, and the branchlets form similar flattened and lacy sprays, though they are often more drooping or stringy. When bruised they give off a similar tansylike odor. The cones are approximately ½ inch long and have leathery, brown scales, about six bearing tiny winged seeds.

The western red cedar is found along the Pacific coast from southeastern Alaska to northwestern California, and eastward into the Rocky Mountains from southeastern British Columbia to northern Idaho and western Montana. It occurs near the coast from sea level to an altitude of 4,000 feet, and at from 2,000 to 7,000 feet in the Rockies. It seldom forms pure stands, but often makes up as much as 50 per cent of mixed coniferous forest.

The strongly aromatic wood is reddish-brown when it is first cut, but turns dull brown on exposure. It is light in weight, moderately soft, and not particularly strong, but highly resistant to decay. Its chief use is for shingles, but it also goes into exterior siding, interior finish, sashes and doors, greenhouse construction, ship and boat-building, and boxes and crates. It is also a leading wood for poles and posts.

The scientific name *plicata* means "folded into plaits," and was no doubt suggested by the arrangement of the leaves on the flattened twigs.

## ATLANTIC WHITE CEDAR (*Chamaecyparis thyoides*)

River swamps and low wet places along the streams of the coastal plain from southern Maine to northern Florida, and westward along the Gulf coast to eastern Louisiana, are the habitat of the Atlantic white cedar. Its leaves are tiny scales $\frac{1}{16}$ to $\frac{1}{8}$ inch long, pressed tightly in overlapping rows against the branchlets like the shingles on a roof. They are a rather dull dark-green, each with a small glandular dot on its back, and the branchlets that bear them are disposed in flattened, feathery sprays. Bruised, they give off a pleasant spicy fragrance.

In New England it might be possible to confuse this tree with the northern white cedar, and elsewhere with the eastern red cedar; but if cones happen to be present there can be little doubt. The cones of the Atlantic white cedar are ball-shaped and about $\frac{1}{4}$ inch in diameter. At first they are light-green, coated with a grayish or whitish bloom. Later they become bluish-purple, and when mature they turn a dark reddish-brown. Usually each one is formed of five shield-shaped scales, arranged in two pairs at right angles to each other, with the odd scale in the middle. These scales are slightly rough and angular, with a weak prickle in the depressed center. The cones mature in one year and contain from five to fifteen seeds with wings at the sides. So tiny are the seeds that between 400,000 and 500,000 weigh only a pound.

An average-sized tree will be 80 to 85 feet in height, with a trunk 10 to 14 inches in diameter, but occasionally one will be as much as 120 feet high with a trunk diameter of 5 feet. The trees often grow in dense, pure stands where swamp peat overlies a sandy subsoil. Such stands, commonly called "juniper glades" or "cedar glades," once covered much larger areas than they do now. In many places all of the marketable trees have been cut or destroyed by fires. A dense undergrowth of tangled vines and shrubs commonly makes passage difficult in white cedar stands.

The wood is light-weight, soft, comparatively weak, and fine-textured, and has a slightly spicy aroma when freshly cut. It is light brown with a red or pinkish tinge and is very durable. Much of it is used for poles and posts, but it is very useful for many other purposes: boats, tanks, siding and interior finish, boxes and crates, shingles, and woodenware.

The Atlantic white cedar is of value as an ornamental tree, too, but is less commonly used than the two western American species or than some others that have been introduced from the Orient. A few horticultural varieties have been developed. This is a fine tree for planting in places too wet for most others to grow.

The name *Chamaecyparis* comes from the Greek name of an Old World shrub, the ground cypress; and *thyoides* means "*Thuja*-like."

## PORT ORFORD CEDAR (*Chamaecyparis lawsoniana*)

The Port Orford cedar is found in a narrow strip along the Pacific coast of southwestern Oregon and northwestern California, where it grows from sea level to an altitude of about 5,000 feet. It is a large tree, often 140 to 180 feet, or sometimes even as much as 225 feet in height, with a trunk commonly 4 to 6 and occasionally as much as 16 feet in diameter. The American Forestry Association's current champion is a tree at Squaw Creek, Coos County, Oregon, with a height of 200 feet and a trunk measuring 27 feet 2 inches in circumference at 4½ feet above the ground.

The trunk of the Port Orford cedar has very thick reddish-brown bark, deeply furrowed into large, fibrous ridges. The tiny, scalelike, bright-green leaves are seldom over 1/16 inch long except on the leading shoots. They grow flat and overlapping along the branchlets. Each one has a glandular spot on the back and is whitened underneath by rows of minute stomata. The branchlets form fine, flattened, lacy or feathery sprays. The rounded, reddish-brown cones are about 1/3 inch in diameter and have three pairs of shield-shaped scales, each of which bears from two to five seeds with pairs of side wings.

The wood of the Port Orford cedar is light yellow to pale brown in color, and is moderately light-weight, hard, and strong, with an even grain and a pleasant, spicy odor. A large proportion of the lumber goes into storage-battery separators and venetian blinds; but it is also used for furniture, flooring, interior finish, sashes, and doors, in boatbuilding, and in the manufacture of mothproof boxes and chests. The demand for the lumber often exceeds the supply.

Port Orford cedar is one of the most attractive ornamental evergreens, and a large number of horticultural varieties have been developed. These include trees of various shapes and sizes, some whose shoots are tipped with creamy-white, others with yellow, golden, or blue-white foliage, and some small varieties that are suitable for planting in rock gardens.

The scientific name *lawsoniana* honors Peter Lawson, an Edinburgh nurseryman who first introduced the tree into cultivation. He and his sons purchased seeds from William Murray, who collected them in California in 1854, and whose brother Andrew Murray first officially named the tree. Sometimes it is called the Lawson cypress, although it is no more a true cypress than it is a true cedar.

## ALASKA YELLOW CEDAR (*Chamaecyparis nootkatensis*)

The Alaska yellow cedar is a smaller tree usually 60 to 90 feet, but sometimes up to 130 feet high, with a trunk usually 2 to 3, or occasionally as much as 6 feet in diameter. It is found in the Pacific coast region from southeastern Alaska to northern California. The trunk has a rather thin, grayish-brown bark which is irregularly fissured, fibrous, and scaly. Its scale-like leaves are about ⅛ inch long, and they usually lack glands; and the shield-shaped scales of its half-inch cones are tipped with spines.

The Alaska yellow cedar produces a valuable wood—usually sold as Alaska cypress, yellow cypress, or yellow cedar—which is used for interior finish, cabinet work, small boats, furniture, and novelties. The species is often grown as an ornamental tree, and several horticultural varieties have been developed.

The name *nootkatensis* indicates that the tree was first discovered at Nootka Sound on Vancouver Island, British Columbia.

## EASTERN RED CEDAR (*Juniperus virginiana*)

Over most of the eastern half of the United States, the eastern red cedar is found on dry hills, in abandoned fields, along fencerows and roadsides, and sometimes even in swamps. Its dense, dark-green, columnlike or cone-shaped form will be familiar to anyone who travels about the countryside. Ordinarily it grows from 20 to about 50 feet tall, with a trunk from 1 to 2 feet in diameter, but occasionally a much larger specimen may be seen. One growing near Roganville, Texas, 76 feet tall and with a breast-high trunk circumference of 12 feet 2 inches, is the champion eastern red cedar as recorded by the American Forestry Association.

The eastern red cedar has two kinds of evergreen leaves. Mostly they are small and scalelike, pressed tight against the branchlet in opposite pairs. On very young trees, and on the more vigorous shoots of older ones, the leaves are awllike and spreading, with sharply pointed tips. Small and inconspicuous "flowers" appear in late winter or early spring, and by fall some of these have developed into what look like dark-blue berries, whitened with a bloom. Actually these are cones with a few fleshy scales; inside they have usually one or two, rarely three or four, seeds without wings. They are relished by several kinds of birds, which are chiefly responsible for scattering the seeds over the countryside. Cedar waxwings, as their name indicates, are especially fond of them.

The trunk of even a fair-sized red cedar is made up mostly of highly aromatic, pinkish-red to deep reddish-brown heartwood, which is surrounded by a very thin layer of nearly white sapwood. Formerly it was the wood principally used for making pencils, and it is used extensively for making chests and wardrobes and for lining closets. Some of it also goes into small boats and scientific instruments. Because the wood is so durable in contact with the ground, it makes very good fence posts. An oil from the leaves is used in medicines, and another from the wood in both medicines and perfumes.

The eastern red cedar is useful, too, for planting in shelterbelts and as an ornamental tree, and a number of horticultural forms have been developed. Some of these have silvery or bluish-green leaves; in others the young shoots are tipped with yellow. One keeps the form of a dense, dwarf bush, and another has "weeping" branchlets.

Apple growers do not like to have red cedar trees in the vicinity of their orchards, for the very good reason that the tree is an alternate host of a rust fungus which is often quite destructive in apple orchards, although serious harm is seldom done to the red cedar. On the red cedar the fungus causes galls—commonly called "cedar apples"—which may be as much as two inches across. They become most conspicuous in the spring when they are covered with protruding, bright-orange, jellylike horns. Spores released by the horns are carried by the wind; and if they happen to alight on the leaves of apples or crabapples, the fungus begins to grow there, causing spots that develop on the leaves and later on the fruits. The fungus must have both hosts to complete its life cycle.

*Juniperus* is the Latin name for the genus of trees to which the red cedar (which, once again, is not a true cedar) belongs. Nine species of juniper are found in the western United States, where they are correctly called "junipers" rather than "cedars." Most of these grow in the driest and rockiest places, and generally they are no more than shrubs or small trees. They may be recognized by their leaves, which are both scalelike and awllike, and by their fleshy, berrylike cones.

The most widely distributed is the Rocky Mountain juniper (*Juniperus scopulorum*), found throughout the Rockies from southern British Columbia and southwestern Alberta south to northwestern Texas and Arizona. Although often shrubby, it occasionally attains a height of 40 to 55 feet, with a trunk 1½ to 3 feet in diameter. The American Forestry Association records one in the Cache National Forest of Utah with a trunk circumference of 26 feet 8 inches at 4½ feet above the ground. The name *scopulorum* means "of rocky cliffs or crags."

The alligator juniper (*Juniperus deppeana*) takes its name from the bark of the older trees, which somewhat resembles an alligator's hide. A full-grown tree may be 30 to 50, or rarely 60 feet high, with a trunk diameter of usually 1½ to 3 or now and then even 6 feet or more. This juniper is found from southwestern Texas westward through the desert ranges to Arizona, and southward into Mexico. The scientific name *deppeana* honors the German botanist Ferdinand Deppe.

The western or sierra juniper (*Juniperus occidentalis*) occurs in the mountains from Washington southward into California and eastward into Montana, Idaho, and Nevada. Although it is usually no more than a shrub or small tree, the American Forestry Association records one in the Stanislaus National Forest of California that is 87 feet high and has a trunk circumference of 42 feet 9 inches. The name *occidentalis* means "western."

# YEW FAMILY

## CALIFORNIA TORREYA (*Torreya californica*)

❧ THE world's species of torreyas can be numbered on the fingers of one hand. Two are found in widely separated sections of the United States —in Florida and in California—and the two others are natives of China and Japan. The genus was named in honor of John Torrey, a noted American botanist of the nineteenth century.

The California torreya, which also goes by the names of stinking cedar and California nutmeg, is found in the Coast Ranges of central California, and on the western slope of the Sierra Nevada up to an altitude of about 6,000 feet. Usually it is a tree from 35 to 80 feet in height, with a trunk from 1 to 3 feet in diameter; but in rare instances one may be much larger. The champion reported by the American Forestry Association is a tree near Mendocino, California, with a height of 141 feet and a trunk circumference of 14 feet 10 inches at 4½ feet above the ground.

Torreyas are members of the yew family, and although their evergreen leaves look like those of some of the conifers, they do not bear cones. Unlike the conifers, the torreyas always produce male or stamen-bearing and female or ovule-bearing "flowers" on separate plants, so that some trees never produce "fruits." The California torreya has stiff, narrow, and flattened leaves, from 1 to about 3 inches long, with sharply pointed tips. They are a dark, shiny yellowish-green on the upper side and have two whitish bands underneath. When crushed, they emit a sharp and rather disagreeable odor.

The "fruits," which look very much like olives but are actually fruits only in the sense that a pine cone is, measure from 1 to 1½ inches in length and are pale yellowish-green with irregular dull-purple areas or streaks. Within the fleshy outer covering is a large seed, whose woody outer coat is wrinkled in such a way that it somewhat resembles a nutmeg.

In color the wood of the torreya is a clear lemon-yellow, and it is moderately light-weight, hard, fine-grained, and very durable. Doubtless it would make a fine cabinet wood were it more plentiful. Little use of it is made today, although the California Indians once employed it for making bows.

## FLORIDA TORREYA (*Torreya taxifolia*)

The Florida torreya is a smaller tree, and a very rare one, found along the Apalachicola River in northwestern Florida and southwestern Georgia.

## PACIFIC YEW (*Taxus brevifolia*)

Yews are familiar to most people as shrubs commonly planted about the foundations of houses. Many who live in the northeastern part of North America are also acquainted with the American yew or ground hemlock (*Taxus canadensis*), a common little understory shrub of the coniferous woods. The Pacific yew, on the other hand, often becomes a fairly sizable tree. Three of the world's eight species of yew are native to North America.

CALIFORNIA TORREYA                    PACIFIC YEW

The Pacific yew is found in the Pacific coast region from southeastern Alaska to northern California, and also in the Sierra Nevada to the central part of the same state. It also occurs in the Rocky Mountain region from southeastern British Columbia south to western Montana, northern Idaho, eastern Washington, and northeastern Oregon. *Taxus* is the classical Latin name for the yew, and *brevifolia* means "short-leaved," the leaves being shorter than those of the English yew.

Normally the Pacific yew is a small tree, 20 to 40 feet high, with a trunk a foot or a little more in diameter. Less commonly it becomes a tree 50 to 60, or rarely 75 feet tall, with a trunk diameter of between 1½ and 2½ feet. The current champion recorded by the American Forestry Association is a tree near Mineral, Lewis County, Washington. It has a height of 59 feet 5 inches, a branch spread of 57 feet, and a trunk that measures 14 feet 8 inches in circumference at 4½ feet above the ground. Except for the largest of old trees, those growing partly or wholly in the open have an open cone-shaped crown which extends nearly or all the way to the ground.

One may recognize the yew by its deep yellowish-green leaves, which are paler underneath, pointed at the tip, soft to the touch, and from ½ to 1 inch long. On trees which have borne the ovules—for yews have no real flowers—bright coral-red "fruits" ripen in September or October. Actually they are not fruits, but hard-coated seeds each borne inside a fleshy cup-like disk, which birds eat and thus scatter the seeds. The trunk of the Pacific yew has a very thin bark composed of thin, papery purple scales which break away exposing the clear rose-colored or purplish-red bark beneath.

The wood of the yew is dense, hard, strong, fine-grained, rather heavy, a clear rose-red in color, and remarkably durable in an unprotected state. It would be excellent for many purposes except for its scarcity, which means that its use is confined mainly to archers' bows, canoe paddles, turned articles, and small cabinet work. Because of its durability it is, of course, suitable for posts and poles.

The third native North American yew is the Florida species (*Taxus floridana*), a small, very rare tree found along the Apalachicola River in northwestern Florida.

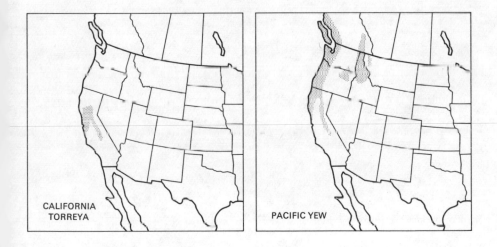

CALIFORNIA
TORREYA

PACIFIC YEW

# PART TWO

## *Angiosperms*

ANGIOSPERMS ARE THE PLANTS WITH TRUE FLOWERS. THE
OVULES ARE PRODUCED WITHIN THE OVARY OF THE PISTIL,
WHICH LATER DEVELOPS INTO A FRUIT CONTAINING THE
SEED OR SEEDS. EMBRYOS OF THE SEEDS OF THE MONOCOTS
HAVE ONE COTYLEDON; FIBROVASCULAR BUNDLES (CON-
DUCTING TISSUES) ARE DISTRIBUTED THROUGHOUT THE
STEMS. EMBRYOS OF THE SEEDS OF THE DICOTS HAVE A
PAIR OF COTYLEDONS; FIBROVASCULAR BUNDLES ARE AR-
RANGED IN A RING ABOUT THE CENTRAL PITH OF THE
STEMS.

# LILY FAMILY

## CABBAGE PALMETTO (*Sabal palmetto*)

❧ ON Smith's Island at the mouth of the Cape Fear River, on North Carolina's southeastern coast, the cabbage palmetto makes its most northerly stand. From there southward it becomes increasingly common along the coasts of South Carolina and Georgia and on the sea islands. Throughout most of Florida it is the commonest and most conspicuous of tree palms. It is the only tree palm to be found north of Florida, and it has the widest range of all native North American palms.

The trunk of the cabbage palmetto usually grows straight and tall, to a maximum height of about 30 feet toward the north, up to 80 or 90 feet in Florida. The American Forestry Association's champion—a tree in Highlands Hammock State Park, Florida—is 90 feet tall and has a trunk measuring 3 feet 9 inches in circumference. At its summit is a big cluster of fan-shaped leaves, from 4 to 7 feet across, folded and divided into many pointed segments, with threadlike fibers between them. The leaves stand on leaf stalks from 5 to 7 feet in length. New leaves in the center of the crown stand erect. Later they spread out horizontally, finally bending downward and turning brown with age. For some years the bases of the old leaf stalks persist on the trunk; but eventually they fall off, leaving a lattice-like network of ridges on the grayish-brown trunk.

Early Spanish explorers found that the Florida Indians ate the large cabbage-like bud growing in the center of the tree's crown. They tried it and found it to be very tender and palatable, and thus the tree with a "cabbage" at its heart got its name. Since that time many people have acquired a taste for the "palm cabbage." Unfortunately the removal of the bud permanently disfigures or even kills the tree—a thing that most people today would not wish to do.

Since early colonial days the trunks of cabbage palmettoes have been prized as pilings of wharves and docks, for the wood of no other tree has

67

such a resistance to the inroads of teredos or shipworms. Early South Carolinians used stout palmetto logs to build a fort on Sullivan's Island in Charleston harbor, where it turned out to be quite impervious to British cannonballs, and where on June 28, 1776, General William Moultrie and his band of volunteers drove off the besieging oaken ships of the British Navy—a victory commemorated on the state seal of South Carolina by an erect palmetto and an uprooted oak. It also earned South Carolina its nickname of "The Palmetto State," and both there and in Florida the cabbage palmetto has since become the state tree.

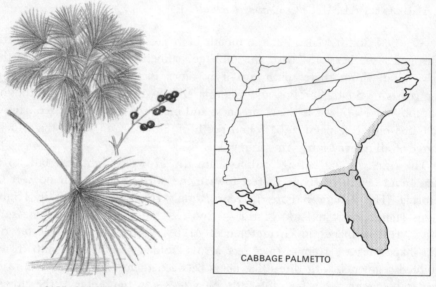

CABBAGE PALMETTO

CABBAGE PALMETTO

In Florida the Seminole Indians still use palmetto trunks to build their houses, and thatch the roofs with the stiff fan-shaped leaves. The fibers of the leaf stalks are used to make brushes and wisk brooms. The leaves are used in mats, baskets, hats, and other woven objects.

In early summer small white flowers appear on the palmettoes in huge clusters 2 or more feet long. The flowers are fragrant and laden with nectar, and thus attract hordes of bees which effect their pollination. By fall they develop into large clusters of roundish, black, plumlike fruits which are about ⅓ of an inch in diameter. They are edible and sweet, and are greatly relished by flocks of wintering robins, by fish crows and raccoons, and by the Seminole Indians.

An attractive tropical-looking tree, the cabbage palmetto is often planted about home grounds, along streets and roadsides, and in the parks of cities near the coast; but unfortunately it does not thrive very far inland north of Florida, although to those who live within its domain it is indeed one of the most familiar of trees.

The age of a cabbage palmetto, or, for that matter, any other kind of palm can only be surmised, for the trunk of a palm has no rings to show its annual growth. A palm trunk is made up of long, threadlike, more or less woody fibers (technically known as fibrovascular bundles), scattered through pithy tissue. It has no true bark on the outside, but only a sort of rind. Conifers and broad-leaved trees have a thin layer of growing cells, called the cambium, on the *outside* of a cylinder of solid wood, lying just beneath the inner bark. Each year this cambium forms a new layer of wood over the layer formed the year before, and the result is a series of rings which show each year's growth. The trunks of palms grow in diameter from the *inside*, usually through the gradual increase in the size of the cells and the spaces between them.

The scientific name *Sabal* is believed to be an American Indian name, and *palmetto* comes from the Spanish word *palmito,* meaning "little palm."

## WASHINGTON PALM (*Washingtonia filifera*)

Named in honor of George Washington, the Washington palm—or, as it is sometimes called, the California palm—is the only tree of that family native to the western United States. In its native haunts it is by no means common, but is scattered in little groves about the margin of the Colorado Desert, an inland sea bed that dried up long ago, and in the low desert mountain canyons of southern California and southwestern Arizona. It also crosses the border into the northern part of Baja California. No other North American palm, however, has traveled so far under cultivation as this one, for it is widely planted in Florida and in cities along the Gulf coast as well as in its native California. It grows in Hawaii, where it is commonly called the hula palm, and in the Mediterranean region of Europe; and it is often grown in greenhouses and conservatories where it could not thrive out of doors.

In a general way the Washington palm resembles the cabbage palmetto of the Southeast. It has a crown of great fan-shaped leaves, often 4½ feet broad and somewhat longer, on stalks 3 to 6 feet in length. The leaves are deeply slashed into stiff, ribbonlike divisions, cleft in two at the ends, with edges frayed into many long, threadlike fibers (the name *filifera* means "thread-bearing"). The flowers and fruits are quite similar to those of the cabbage palmetto, but the leaf stalks of the Washington palm are armed along both edges with irregular, sharp, and often hooked spines.

Commonly this palm reaches a height of 35 to 50 feet, or sometimes as much as 60 or 70 feet. The trunk is often 2 or 3 feet in diameter, tapered very gradually—often almost imperceptibly—and a thatchlike "skirt" of dead leaves often hangs to within a few feet of the ground. Frequently the trunks are scarred by fire, to which the tree is subject until the covering of dead leaves has been consumed. The trees themselves endure burning without apparent injury, and continue to grow thriftily afterward.

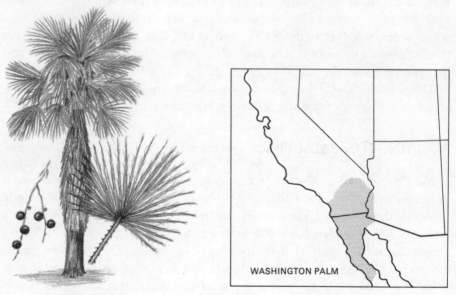

WASHINGTON PALM

WASHINGTON PALM

## FLORIDA ROYAL PALM (*Roystonea elata*)

No other tree in the southern part of Florida is more likely to attract the attention of a visitor than the stately royal palm whose trunk grows straight and tall, looking for all the world like a smooth gray column of concrete. But within 8 or 10 feet of the top the trunk tapers and becomes bright green, ending in a massive crown of arching, deep-green, featherlike leaves. Among native palms it has no peer.

William Bartram was undoubtedly the first naturalist to behold this magnificent tree, though he did not see it at the southern tip of the Florida peninsula where it is found today. Rather, he found the tree growing along the St. John's River, between what are now Volusia and Lake counties, well up toward the northern part of the state. In fact, that was about as far south in Florida as the Quaker traveler ever got, but in his *Travels* he gave the first description of the Florida royal palm, and a very accurate one. Nobody has ever reported it growing so far north since Bartram's time, and it is presumed that the species did not survive the extremely cold winter of 1835.

Royal palms grow to a height of 80 to 100 feet, and the trunk often reaches

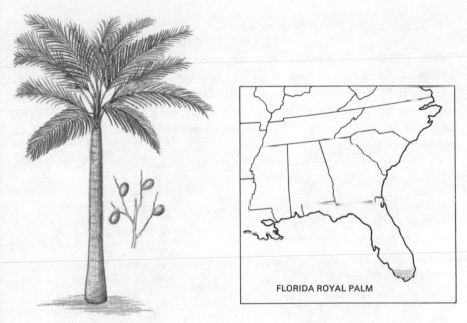

FLORIDA ROYAL PALM

FLORIDA ROYAL PALM

a diameter of 2 feet. The huge leaves, measuring from 10 to 12 feet long, are cut like feathers into numerous strap-shaped segments, the largest 2½ to 3 feet in length but gradually decreasing in size toward the tip of the leaf. The upper portion of the trunk appears green because it is enclosed by the sheathlike green bases of the leaf stalks. In spring the small white flowers are produced, in dense, branched, drooping clusters that are often 2 feet long; and in summer they are followed by clusters of half-inch, egg-shaped, violet-blue fruits resembling small plums.

In recent years the wild royal palm has been confined to rich, moist hammocks in Collier, Dade, and Monroe counties, where the trees rear their crowns of immense leaves far above the surrounding vegetation. In its natural state the tree can be seen both in Collier Seminole State Park and in Everglades National Park, but there are fine avenues of this stately palm in many towns and along many of the highways of south Florida. It is a tree that once seen will never be forgotten. *Roystonea,* the scientific name of the genus to which all royal palms belong, honors General Roy Stone, a United States Army engineer who rendered outstanding service in Puerto Rico during the Spanish-American War. The name *elata,* given by William Bartram, means "tall" or "elevated."

## JOSHUA TREE (*Yucca brevifolia*)

The oddest of all American trees are to be met with in the deserts of the Southwest. They do not look at all like ordinary trees, but no ordinary tree could survive where these strange plants thrive. One of them is the Joshua tree, a weird-looking member of the lily family, which grows in the Mohave Desert from southwestern Utah and southern Nevada to western Arizona and southern California.

Ordinarily a Joshua tree is 15 to 30, or rarely 40 feet high, with a trunk

JOSHUA TREE

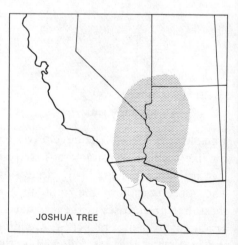

JOSHUA TREE

from less than a foot to 2 or occasionally 3 feet in diameter. The trunk divides into big, clumsy-looking branches which bristle with bayonetlike leaves. As the leaves die they become pressed downward, forming a thick, thatchlike covering on the younger trunks and branches. A Joshua tree looks about as formidable as a porcupine. There is nothing quite like it. According to tradition, the Mormons gave the unique tree its name, perhaps because they saw a likeness to a bearded Old Testament patriarch with his arms uplifted to heaven.

Joshua trees grow very slowly, but it is impossible to know just how old one is since the trunk, like that of a palm, has no tell-tale rings by which its age might be determined. Also, the pith tends to disintegrate, leaving mere bundles of woody fibers about a hollow center. Large Joshua trees, however, are estimated to be from 100 to 300 years old, and some may, of course, be even older.

In April or May, dense, branched clusters of greenish-yellow to cream-colored bell-shaped flowers—with a not very pleasant odor—appear at the ends of the branches. Like those of other members of the genus *Yucca,* the Joshua tree's flowers are pollinated by a little Pronuba moth, of a species peculiar to the Joshua tree. When the female moth is ready to lay her eggs, she gathers a ball of sticky pollen from the anthers and presses it on the stigma portion of the pistil, exactly as though she understood the necessity of pollination. As soon as the tiny larvae hatch from the eggs she has laid on the pistil, they bore inside the ovary, where they feed on the tissues of the developing fruits and on some of the numerous seeds. Without the help of the Pronuba moth, there would never be any fruits and seeds on a Joshua tree; and only the Joshua tree can provide food for the moth's larvae. The two are mutually dependent upon each other.

To preserve this extraordinary tree, more than 800 square miles of desert in southern California have been set aside as the Joshua Tree National Monument. More recently the Arizona Highway Department has designated seventeen miles of forest along Highway 93 as the Arizona Joshua Forest Parkway. At one time several newspapers in this country and Great Britain bought stock in an enterprise intended to make paper pulp from Joshua trees. Fortunately the pulp proved to be of a poor quality; the project was abandoned, and a comparatively rare species was spared.

*Yucca* is from the Carib Indian name for the root of a related plant, and Linnaeus assigned it to this genus. *Brevifolia,* meaning "short-leaved," was assigned because the leaves of the Joshua tree are shorter than those of most other yuccas.

# WILLOW FAMILY

## BLACK WILLOW (*Salix nigra*)

❧ OF the many species of willows that grow in North America, a comparative few ever attain the stature of trees; but of those that do, the black willow is by far the largest, and the only one big enough to produce wood of commercial importance. It grows on moist or wet soils around lakes, along streams, and in swamps from Nova Scotia west to southern Ontario and eastern North Dakota, and southward into Georgia, Mississippi, and eastern Texas.

In some places the black willow is hardly much more than a large shrub; yet it can become a tree 30 to 40 feet high, with a trunk up to a foot in diameter. Sometimes it reaches truly magnificent proportions: a height of up to 120 feet and a trunk 4 or more feet in diameter. The current champion, according to the American Forestry Association, is a tree at Traverse City, Michigan. The trunk has a circumference of 26 feet 1 inch at 4½ feet above ground, is 85 feet high, and has a limb spread of 79 feet.

More often than not, the trunk of a black willow divides into great branches at or close to the ground, so that several trees appear to grow in a clump. As a rule a black willow trunk is crooked; almost invariably it is inclined at an angle, and it is covered with rough, thick-scaled, blackish-brown bark. The tree has a broad, open, and more or less irregular round-topped crown. Its slender and drooping branchlets are brittle at the base and thus easily broken off.

In spring, the flowers appear in slender clusters at the ends of short leafy shoots; those that bear stamens and those that bear pistils are always on separate trees. Each of the former has from three to five stamens; in the latter, the pistil is solitary. Both kinds of flower have the form of a little scale with a nectar gland at its base, so that willows, unlike their relatives the aspens and poplars, attract bees and other insects which carry their heavy, sticky pollen. Within a few weeks the pistil-bearing flowers develop into little bottle-shaped capsules which split open and release the seeds, each with a silky tuft of hairs. Thus the seeds are carried away by the winds, but unless one alights in a suitable place for growth, the tiny embryo within it soon dies.

Although willow trees produce seeds in great abundance, very few are likely to find a spot of moist soil in which they can grow. But the black willow does not rely entirely upon reproduction by seeds. Its brittle branchlets are often broken off by winds and carried down stream by the water, to become lodged along the banks where they can take root and grow. In addition, the black willow often produces sprouts or suckers from its roots, or from trunks that have been uprooted by floods or winds. One of the greatest services it renders is the prevention of the erosion of stream banks and levees.

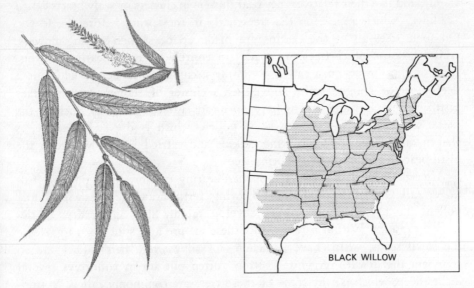

BLACK WILLOW

BLACK WILLOW

In summer the black willow may be known by its slender, lance-shaped leaves, which have finely toothed edges and long-pointed tips. They are 3 to 6 inches in length, green on both sides, and somewhat shiny on the upper surface. In winter the slender, reddish-brown-to-orange twigs have tiny buds scattered along them, each one covered by a solitary reddish-brown scale, which is pointed at the tip.

This tree usually attains its greatest size in the Mississippi Valley, and most of the willow lumber cut in the United States comes from Louisiana northward to southern Missouri and Illinois. The wood of the black willow is lightweight, moderately soft, and uniform in texture, but lacks strength. A special use for it is the making of artificial limbs. Other uses are for furniture, baskets, coffins, boxes, and crates. Willow wood makes a high-grade charcoal, and for this purpose it was much in demand during the days when black powder was used in artillery and firearms.

*Salix* is the classical Latin name for the willow, and *nigra,* meaning "black," perhaps refers to the tree's dark-colored bark.

# Aspens and Poplars

Aspens and poplars, along with the willows, are members of the willow family, and like their relatives they bear flowers in clusters of scaly bracts called "catkins," which appear on the trees early in the spring before the leaves. On some trees all of the catkins are made up of stamen-bearing flowers, while those on other trees are made up entirely of pistil-bearing flowers. Each of the flowers in a catkin is simply a cuplike disk below which is a deeply cut or fringed scale, and either a cluster of stamens or a solitary pistil. The poplars and aspens have no means attracting insects, such as the nectar glands of the willows. Their pollen, which is dry and dustlike, is shaken out of the stamen-bearing catkins and carried by the winds to the pistil-bearing catkins on neighboring trees.

After the pollen is spent, the stamen-bearing catkins, their purpose fulfilled, fall from the trees. But following fertilization by the wind-borne pollen, the pistil-bearing flowers develop rapidly into little, dry, bottle-shaped capsules. Within a few weeks these mature and split open to release the small seeds, which have parachutes of silky white hairs. They are so abundant that masses of white "cotton" often pile up in windrows several inches deep, which is why some of these trees are commonly called "cotton-woods." The minute embryos within the seeds are very short-lived. Unless the seeds find places where they can germinate almost immediately, they will not be able to grow. Only a very few out of a million seeds are likely to become seedling trees.

In addition to the native species, two Old World poplars are familiar in North America. One is the Lombardy poplar (*Populus nigra* var. *italica*), which is distinguished by its narrow, tall, spirelike crown. The other is the white poplar (*Populus alba*), whose maplelike leaves are dark green above and felted with a glistening white down beneath.

*Populus* is the classical Latin name for an aspen or poplar tree.

## QUAKING ASPEN (*Populus tremuloides*)

The far-flung empire of the quaking aspen stretches from Newfoundland and Labrador westward across Canada, along the northern limit of tree growth, to northwestern Alaska. In the eastern part of the United States it ranges southward to northern Virginia and northeastern Missouri; in the west it follows the mountain ranges south into northern Mexico and southern California. This is probably the most widely distributed of all North American trees.

Young quaking aspens are distinguished by their smooth yellowish-green-to-whitish bark, which is often marked with blackish scars. On the bases of the trunks of older trees the bark becomes black and thick, with flat ridges separated by furrows. The tree gets its name from the almost incessant quivering of its small, roundish to broadly egg-shaped, sharp-pointed and finely toothed leaves, whose slender stalks are flattened as though they had been pinched inward from the sides. The name *tremuloides*, from the Latin word for "trembling," means "like *Populus tremula*" (the European aspen).

Quaking aspens are relatively short-lived, fast-growing trees, and seldom attain a height of more than 50 or 60 feet, with a trunk from 1 to 2 feet in diameter. Occasionally one will be as much as 100 feet tall, with a trunk diameter of 3 feet. The present champion recorded by the American Forestry Association is a tree in Santa Fe National Forest, New Mexico, which is 70 feet in height and has a breast-high trunk circumference of 11 feet 6 inches.

Aspens quickly pioneer on cut-over or burned-over forest lands, or in abandoned fields, where they often occur in nearly pure stands. Usually, however, the aspen forest is a temporary thing. Hardwood trees such as red and sugar maples, yellow birches, beeches—and sometimes various conifers —slowly develop in the protecting shade cast by their branches, and eventually outstrip the aspens, succeeding them if fires do not intervene. In primeval forests, aspens occur only as scattered trees, most often along streams and in places where the forest cover is sparse.

The wood of the aspens is soft, light, and rather weak. It is used as pulpwood and for making boxes and crates, excelsior, matches, and various small turned articles. Wherever it grows, the bark of the quaking aspen is a preferred food of the beaver. By choice these animal engineers always locate their dams and build their lodges where there are stands of aspen trees; and often, when the supply in the immediate vicinity runs out, they construct canals to more distant groves of aspen.

In fall the leaves of the quaking aspen turn a bright golden-yellow, which is usually the most brilliant patch of color in western woodlands at that season. This is often the only hardwood tree present in western forests, which are predominantly made up of conifers.

## BIGTOOTH ASPEN (*Populus grandidentata*)

The bigtooth aspen of the northeastern United States and adjacent Canada, grows southward in the Appalachians to western North Carolina and eastern Tennessee. It may be recognized in summer by its coarsely wavy-toothed leaves, and in winter by its stouter twigs and dusty-gray buds. The name *grandidentata* means "big-toothed."

## BALSAM POPLAR (*Populus balsamifera*)

One of the most characteristic trees of the North Woods, the balsam poplar ranges westward from the shores of Labrador and northern New England to northwestern Alaska. It grows as far north as the limit of tree growth, but extends only as far southward as New York, Michigan, and Minnesota in the East, and to western South Dakota, Colorado, Wyoming, and Idaho in the West. Small, isolated colonies are found locally a bit farther south, and are doubtless the remnant of much more extensive stands that flourished in earlier post-glacial times. This is the "cottonwood" chosen by Wyoming as its state tree.

In winter it is possible to recognize the balsam poplar by its reddish-brown-to-dark-brown polished twigs, on which are buds saturated with a fragrant, amber-colored resin. The name *balsamifera* means "balsam-bearing." In summer the species may be known by its egg-shaped leaves, which are a lustrous dark green above and a paler green beneath, and are edged with fine roundish teeth. They are from 3 to 6 inches long and stand on rounded leaf stalks. On the older trunks the greenish-brown or reddish-brown bark becomes grayish and furrowed, with flat, scaly ridges.

Most often this is a tree 60 to 80 feet in height, with a trunk 1 to 2 feet in diameter. Typically a tree of bottomlands and stream banks, it attains its greatest size in the Mackenzie River Valley of northwestern Canada. There it sometimes reaches a height of 100 feet, with a trunk from 4 to 6 feet in diameter. It develops a long cylindrical trunk and a narrow, open, pyramid-shaped crown.

Woodsmen often call this tree the balm of Gilead, a name botanists and horticulturists reserve for one of its varieties, which has very broadly heart-shaped leaves, more or less hairy on the undersides, with hairy leaf stalks. This variety is commonly planted as a shade tree in Canada and the northern United States, and is propagated by cuttings or root sprouts. The soft wood is excellent for paper pulp and is sometimes used to make boxes and crates. The clear, fragrant resin from the buds has been used as an ointment and as an ingredient of cough medicines.

## BLACK COTTONWOOD (*Populus trichocarpa*)

Not only is the black cottonwood the largest of our American poplars, but it is also the largest broad-leaved tree in the forests of the Pacific Northwest. It is found in forests from southern Alaska and the Yukon southward to southern California and western Nevada, as well as locally in Wyoming and southwestern North Dakota.

Under the best growing conditions the black cottonwood is usually a tree 80 to 100 feet high, with a trunk from 3 to 4 feet in diameter; but in the Puget Sound basin and adjacent areas, trees from 175 to 225 feet in height, with trunks 7 or 8 feet in diameter, have been found. The current champion listed by the American Forestry Association—one near Haynes, Alaska—is 101 feet in height and has a trunk circumference of 32 feet 6 inches at 4½ feet above the ground.

Sometimes this tree is called the western balsam poplar, and strictly speaking it is a balsam poplar rather than a cottonwood. Its broadly egg-shaped leaves are usually 3 to 6 inches long, with finely toothed margins. They are a shiny dark green above, silvery-white to pale green or rusty-brown beneath, and have leaf stalks that are round in cross section. The orange-brown to greenish-brown twigs bear pointed buds, which are coated with a fragrant yellowish-brown resin. Older trunks have a grayish bark, which becomes deeply furrowed, with narrow, flat-topped ridges. The name *trichocarpa* means "hairy-fruited," and refers to the seed capsules.

The wood of this tree is light, soft, and weak, like that of its relatives. It is used principally for pulpwood, excelsior, woodenware, boxes, and crates.

## NARROWLEAF COTTONWOOD (*Populus augustifolia*)

The narrowleaf cottonwood is one of the trees discovered by Lewis and Clark on their journey up the Missouri River, during the month of June, 1805. We now know that it grows from southern Saskatchewan and Alberta

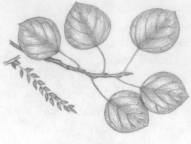

QUAKING ASPEN

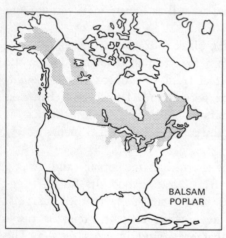

BALSAM POPLAR

EASTERN COTTONWOOD

EASTERN COTTONWOOD

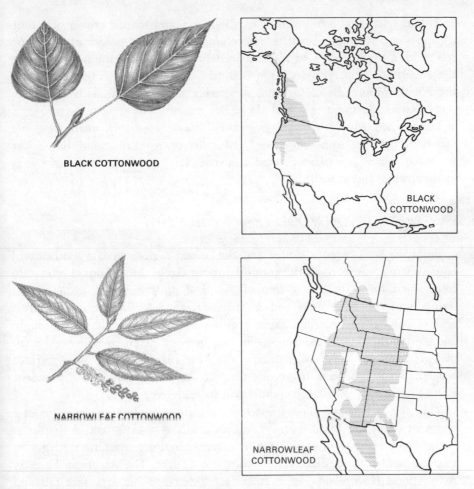

BLACK COTTONWOOD

BLACK COTTONWOOD

NARROWLEAF COTTONWOOD

NARROWLEAF COTTONWOOD

southward through the Rocky Mountain region into Mexico, and on the high plains to the Black Hills and western Nebraska, as well as in the mountains of Nevada and southeastern Oregon. Usually it is found along streams between altitudes of 5,000 and 10,000 feet.

At first glance one might mistake the tree for a willow, since its leaves are narrow and lance-shaped like those of most willows (hence the name *angustifolia,* meaning "narrow-leaved.") They are usually 2 to 4 inches long, and ½ to about 1 inch wide, bright yellowish-green on the upper surface and paler beneath. They have saw-toothed edges, and their short, round stalks and midribs are yellow. The buds on the slender twigs, however, reveal that this is no willow. They are long-pointed; the five scales that cover them are very much coated with resin; and, especially in the springtime, they exhale a strong balsamlike odor.

This is a handsome tree with a narrowly pyramid-shaped crown of strong though slender upright branches. It commonly attains a height of 40 to 60 feet, with a trunk from 1 to 1½ feet in diameter. The champion recorded by the American Forestry Association is a tree on Little Cottonwood Creek in the Pueblo Mountains of Oregon, measuring 55 feet high, with a trunk 6 feet in circumference at 4½ feet above the ground.

Lumbermen pay little or no attention to this relatively small tree, but locally it provides some posts and poles. In towns throughout the Rocky Mountain region it is often planted as a street tree, and it is worthy of use as an ornamental tree as well.

## EASTERN COTTONWOOD (*Populus deltoides*)

From the St. Lawrence Valley and the coastal regions of the southeastern United States westward to the foothills of the Rocky Mountains, the eastern cottonwood grows in the bottomlands and along streams. It is not at all common in the Northeast, and is absent from most of the Appalachian region; but west of the mountains it grows in greater abundance. Throughout the plains and prairie states, winding belts of green cottonwoods mark the presence of every watercourse. The tree played a role in America's western expansion, and in recollection of its usefulness to the pioneers, Kansas has made the eastern cottonwood its state tree.

This, the largest and most important of eastern poplars, often becomes a tree 80 to 100 feet high, with a trunk as much as 3 or 4 feet in diameter. West of the Mississippi it grows still larger, sometimes attaining a height of 175 feet, with a trunk diameter of from 5 to 11 feet. The American Forestry Association's champion—a tree at Wayne, Michigan—is 131 feet tall and has a trunk 25 feet 9 inches in circumference at 4½ feet above the ground. It usually has a short but massive trunk, often divided near the ground, and it develops a wide-spreading, rounded crown when growing in the open. Its growth is rapid for the first fifty years or so; then the rate of growth declines. Although one may live for a hundred years or more, after an age of about seventy years it begins to deteriorate rapidly. The root system is so shallow that these trees often become victims of high winds, so that very old cottonwoods are quite rare.

In summer the eastern cottonwood may be distinguished by its triangular leaves, from 3 to 7 inches in width, which are glossy green above and paler beneath, and have somewhat curved teeth on their margins. When crushed they give off a rather pleasant balsamic odor. The stalks of the leaves are flattened as if pressed in from the sides, so as to quiver in even the slightest breeze. In fall the leaves turn yellow before being shed. Throughout the winter the shiny brown buds, coated with a sticky resin, give off an odor similar to that of the crushed leaves. The scientific name *deltoides,* from the Greek letter Delta, refers to the triangular shape of the leaves.

On the plains and prairies of the West, the presence of cottonwoods determined the location of pioneer homesteads. Here they afforded shade from the burning midsummer sun and provided firewood to stave off the winter's frequent subzero cold. They provided logs for building houses and stockades. Even the leaves were useful as feed for the settlers' livestock. Cottonwoods have been widely planted in the West ever since, both for windbreaks and as shade trees.

The wood of this tree is rather soft and weak, and warps badly during seasoning, but it is easy to work. As lumber or veneer it is used principally for baskets, boxes, and crates. Some of it is used to make excelsior and as pulpwood for paper mills. But on the whole, it cannot be said that the eastern cottonwood is a very important timber tree.

# WALNUT FAMILY

❧ THE familiar nut trees, the walnuts and hickories, are both members of the walnut family. They all have aromatic compound leaves, which are arranged alternately along the branchlets. The flowers of these trees appear rather late in the spring, as the new leafy shoots are pushing out of the winter buds. Those that bear the stamens are conspicuously clustered in fairly large drooping catkins, and come from buds on twigs developed the previous year. The stamen-bearing catkins of the hickories are always three-branched and quite slender; and the little flowers beneath each catkin scale have a lobed calyx and from three to ten stamens. Those of the walnuts have from eight to as many as forty stamens; the catkins that bear them are stouter, and are never branched.

To find the pistil-bearing flowers one must look at the tips of the new leafy shoots. They are not very large, and each one has a little calyx and a pistil with two plumelike stigmas, ready to catch some of the wind-borne pollen. Both stamen-bearing and pistil-bearing flowers are produced on the same tree.

Prior to the Ice Age, both walnuts and hickories were widely distributed throughout the Northern Hemisphere. Today there are about a dozen species of walnuts, and six of these are found in the United States. The so-called English walnuts sold in grocery stores are from an old World species (*Juglans regia*), which is widely cultivated today in California and Oregon.

We have fared even better so far as hickories are concerned. Of the fifteen or so known species, about a dozen are found in eastern North America, two in China and Indo-China and another in the highlands of Mexico.

## BLACK WALNUT (*Juglans nigra*)

Since pioneer days, the black walnut has been one of the best-known of all American trees. It grows—or rather it grew—quite commonly in forests stretching from Vermont westward to South Dakota, and southward into the

Northern portions of the Gulf states and Texas. Throughout most of this area it still persists today, not only in forests but in isolated woodlots, along roadsides and fencerows, and as a shade tree in many a dooryard. Today a black walnut 70 to 90 feet tall, with a trunk 2 or 3 feet in diameter, is considered a big tree. But in the virgin forests, trees 100 to 150 feet tall, with trunks up to 6 feet in diameter, were not at all unusual. Many such trees had trunks free of branches 50 or 60 feet above the ground. Very few of these have survived to the present day. One that has—a champion in the American Forestry Association's register of big trees—stands in Anne Arundel County, Maryland. It is 108 feet high with a branch spread of 128 feet, and its trunk has a circumference of 20 feet 3 inches at 4½ feet above ground.

Black walnut has always ranked as America's finest cabinet wood. Light to dark brown in color, it is heavy, hard, strong, and stiff, yet easily worked with tools. The early colonists soon knew of its virtues. They used it to make all kinds of furniture, cabinets, and staircases in both town and country houses —but that was not all. Since walnut wood is also durable, many big walnut logs were squared and used for beams in barns, or split up and made into fence rails, back in the days when plenty of big walnut trees still stood in the woods.

Today black walnut brings premium prices. Buyers search for it everywhere, and often even make offers for dooryard trees, or buy the stumps of trees that were cut many years ago. The greater part of the wood available now is cut into veneer for making furniture and cabinets; but black walnut is, and always has been, the wood most prized for gun stocks, a purpose for which it is ideal because of its remarkable ability to withstand blows without splintering, and because its beautiful finish can be maintained with comparative ease.

The leaves of the black walnut are 1 to 2 feet long. They are divided into from fifteen to twenty-three lance-shaped leaflets with finely saw-toothed margins. In April or May, when the new leafy shoots are fairly well developed, flowers appear on the branches; and if all goes well, the pistil-bearing flowers will become ball-shaped fruits up to 2½ inches in diameter, which are a light yellowish-green before the nuts ripen in the fall.

The distinctive flavor of the nuts' oily kernels has long been familiar in American households; but to obtain the kernels it is first necessary to remove the thick and more or less pulpy outer hulls—a job that stains the hands a deep brown. No amount of washing will remove the stain; it simply has to be worn off. From the hulls the pioneers extracted a brown dye which they used to color homespun cloth. Next, after the hulls are removed, comes the arduous task of extricating the nutmeats from their bony and deeply sculptured shells. The reward of all this labor is the delicious flavor lent by the nutmeats to candies, cookies, and ice cream. Today, however, one can buy a package or hermetically sealed can of black walnut meats at the corner store or supermarket.

Every fall the Boy Scouts do a good turn by gathering walnuts from beneath the trees at Washington's Mount Vernon and Jefferson's Monticello, after which they are distributed to Scout troops throughout the country for planting. It is easy to plant a walnut tree. All one has to do is drop the nut, hull and all, into a hole a few inches deep and cover it up; but the nuts must not be allowed to dry out before they are planted.

*Juglans,* the classical Latin name for a walnut tree, means literally "the acorn of Jupiter." The dark wood of the black walnut, as well as the blackish shells of its nuts, are reflected in the name *nigra,* which means "black."

## BUTTERNUT (*Juglans cinerea*)

Wherever the butternut—or white walnut—grows, country people know it well. The early settlers made much use of it, as did the Indians before them. But to city-dwellers, it is not nearly as well known as its cousin the black walnut.

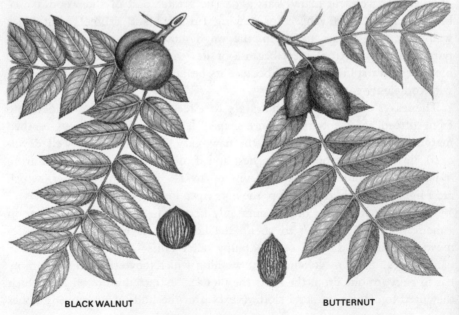

BLACK WALNUT                    BUTTERNUT

The butternut is found from New Brunswick and Maine westward through southern Ontario to Minnesota, thence southward to northern Georgia, Mississippi, and northern Arkansas. In the open it is usually a short-trunked and spreading tree from 30 to 60 feet in height, with a trunk from 1 to 2 feet in diameter. In the forest, particularly on the moist and fertile sites, it sometimes grows to heights of 80 to 100 feet, with a trunk diameter of 3 or 4 feet, but specimens of this size are rather rare. The American Forestry Association reports a champion from St. Joseph County, Michigan, measuring 85 feet in height, with a branch spread of 92 feet and a trunk 11 feet 9 inches in circumference at 4½ feet above the ground.

The butternut may be recognized by its aromatic leaves, which are 15 to 30 inches long and divided into eleven to nineteen leaflets. Both the leaf stalks and the lower surfaces of the leaflets are sticky-hairy. The nuts, which grow in clusters of two to five, are oblong-shaped, 1½ to 2 inches long, and covered with a sticky-hairy green husk. They have a fairly thin bony shell, which is deeply and irregularly ridged on the outside. The kernels within are sweet and highly flavored, but so oily that they very soon become rancid. In winter a butternut tree may be known by its greenish-gray twigs, which have large three-lobed leaf scars with a downy pad or "mustache" on the upper margin, and by the long, downy bud at the tip of each twig. The trunk has gray to blackish bark with broad, flat, light gray ridges forming an irregularly diamond-shaped pattern. The name *cinerea*, meaning "ash-colored," refers to the bark.

The uses made of the butternut have been many. The Indians made sugar from the sap of the tree and pressed a highly prized oil from the nuts. The early settlers used both the husks of the nuts and the inner bark of the

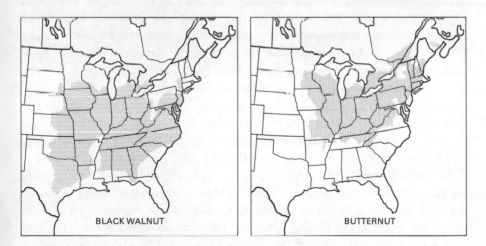

BLACK WALNUT                    BUTTERNUT

tree to dye homespun cloth a rich orange-brown or tan. Even as late as the Civil War, some backwoods regiments went into battle wearing uniforms of homespun cloth colored with butternut dye. The inner bark of the roots has often been used as a mild cathartic; and the young fruits—while still soft enough to be easily pierced with a knitting needle—were often pickled with vinegar, sugar, and spices by frugal country housewives.

The light-brown wood of the butternut is softer, weaker, and much less durable than that of the black walnut, but when polished it shows a beautiful grain and has a satiny luster. It is sometimes used for furniture and cabinet work and has often been used for paneling. Many beautiful altars in older American churches were made from the wood of the butternut.

## SHAGBARK HICKORY (*Carya ovata*)

The shagbark hickory is one of the best known of all our native trees. It grows in forests and woodlots, along fencerows and roadsides, and often in pastures, from southern Maine across southern Ontario to southeastern Minnesota, and in uplands southward into northern Georgia and eastern Texas. Wherever it grows, it is readily recognized by its gray bark, which breaks into long, thin plates that curve away from the trunk, giving it a singular appearance for which shagbark is certainly an appropriate name.

In the open the shagbark has a large and typically oblong crown, which reaches well down toward the ground; but in the forest it develops a clear, straight, cylindrical trunk with a much smaller crown. In forests and woodlots the shagbark is found growing with other kinds of hickories and with various oaks. Usually it is a moderate-sized tree, up to 70 or 80 feet high, with a trunk 1 to 2 feet in diameter; but occasionally it attains a height of 120 feet, with a trunk diameter of as much as 4 feet. A tree at Chevy Chase, Maryland, is the current champion recorded by the American Forestry Association. It is 100 feet in height, with a limb spread of 113 feet, and its trunk at 4½ feet above ground is 11 feet 5 inches in circumference.

The leaves of the shagbark hickory are 8 to 14 inches long and are usually divided into five leaflets, which are lance-shaped or somewhat broader above the middle. During the summer they are a dark yellowish-green; in the fall, like the leaves of most hickories, they turn a bright golden yellow.

In autumn, usually after the first heavy frost, the thick husk surrounding the nut splits into four sections, which tumble to the ground, along with the nut they contained. Squirrels, however, usually do not wait for the nuts to ripen, but often begin cutting them off the trees in late summer. Hickory nuts are a special favorite of the "bannertails," and in fall many squirrels work overtime gathering them and hiding them beneath the carpet of fallen leaves on the forest floor. Many of the nuts they hide are never retrieved to be eaten, but sprout and grow into hickory trees. This is the way most of the hickory trees in the woods today were planted.

The nuts of the shagbark are roundish and slightly flattened, with a sharp little point at one end. Their yellowish-brown to pale reddish-brown, bony shells are fairly thin, and the kernels within are sweet and deliciously flavored. Country people used to gather them in the fall much more than they do today, for use in cakes and candies. The Indians prized hickory nuts very highly. William Bartram tells in his *Travels* of having seen upward of a hundred bushels of hickory nuts that belonged to a single Creek family. He and other early travelers in primitive America have told how the Indians pounded the nuts into pieces and stirred them, shells and all, into boiling water to make a milky liquor. This the Indians called "powcohicora," and from that Indian word "hickory" was presumably derived.

The wood of the shagbark, and of other hickories, is well known for its great strength and toughness. It is—and always has been—the preferred wood for the handles of certain tools, and large quantities of hickory were formerly used to make spokes and rims for wagon and buggy wheels, buggy shafts, and singletrees. Among its other uses are agricultural implements, ladder rungs, archers' bows, gymnasium apparatus, and furniture. For smoking meats it is the best wood obtainable. Hickory-smoked hams and bacon have had a high reputation since early colonial days.

*Carya* comes from the Greek name for "nut," and *ovata*, meaning "ovate" or "egg-shaped," refers to the fruits.

## MOCKERNUT HICKORY (*Carya tomentosa*)

The mockernut is comparatively rare in the northern part of the United States, but it is one of the commonest hickories in the Southeast. It is found to some extent from Massachusetts west through extreme southern Ontario to southeastern Iowa, and southward to northern Florida and eastern Texas. Although it is common on dry upland slopes, usually in company with various oaks, it also is found in the more fertile bottomlands. In the Great Smoky Mountains, and elsewhere in the southern Appalachians, it grows at altitudes up to about 2,800 feet. On the wind-swept, sandy dunes of the South Carolina coast it mingles with live oak and yaupon holly in a forest of dwarf trees.

Quite commonly the mockernut is a tree 50 to 75 feet, or more rarely 90 feet in height, with a trunk 1 or 2, or occasionally 3 feet in diameter. A champion reported by the American Forestry Association grows at Sandy

Spring, Montgomery County, Maryland. It has a height of 112 feet, and the trunk measures 9 feet 2 inches in circumference at 4½ feet above ground. Most often the mockernut is a tall, short-limbed tree with a narrow or oblong crown, although some trees develop broader and more round-topped crowns.

The grayish bark of the mockernut is tight-fitting and never shaggy, but it becomes roughened by irregular furrows separating scaly ridges. The leaves, 8 to 20 inches long, divided into from five to nine but usually seven leaflets, are dark yellowish-green and shiny on the upper surface and paler and downy beneath. The scientific name *tomentosa* means "covered with short matted hairs." A characteristic that helps in recognizing the tree in winter is the early shedding of the outer bud scales, exposing the silky scales that lie beneath them.

The mockernut is so called because the nuts, although often of a good size, have thick shells and comparatively small kernels. Pale, reddish-brown, and nearly spherical but slightly flattened and angled, the nuts measure from 1 to about 1¾ inches long. They are surrounded by a thick husk, which splits into four sections when the nuts ripen, usually in October. The kernels are sweet and have a very fine flavor. Its wood is quite similar to that of the shagbark hickory and is used for the same purposes.

SHAGBARK HICKORY

SHAGBARK HICKORY

**MOCKERNUT HICKORY**

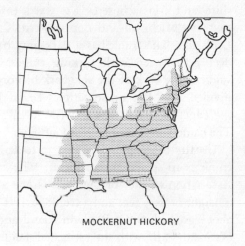

MOCKERNUT HICKORY

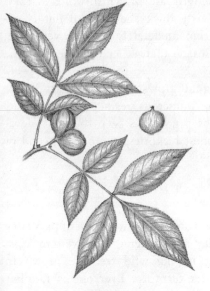

**PIGNUT HICKORY**

PIGNUT HICKORY

## PIGNUT HICKORY (*Carya glabra*)

The pignut hickory is found in woodlands from southern New Hampshire and Massachusetts westward through extreme southern Ontario to southern Michigan and northeastern Kansas, and southward to Florida and Louisiana. The trunk has a dark-gray bark which is usually close-fitting and deeply furrowed with forking ridges, although sometimes it is flaky and suggests the bark of the shagbark hickory. The leaves are 6 to 12 inches long, divided into five or sometimes seven leaflets. They are finely toothed on the edges, shiny dark yellowish-green above, and are usually quite smooth. The name *glabra* means "without hairs."

Usually the pignut is a tree 50 to 60, or occasionally 90 feet high, with a trunk 2 to 4 feet in diameter. The champion in the American Forestry Association's roster of big trees is one at Baton Rouge, Louisiana, which has a height of 165 feet and a trunk 11 feet 5 inches in circumference at 4½ feet above ground. S. G. Baldwin found another in the Great Smoky Mountains National Park with an estimated height of 125 feet and a trunk circumference of 11 feet 3 inches.

The nuts produced by the pignut are sometimes bitter, sometimes quite sweet. They vary from 1 to 2 inches in length, are brownish-white in color and usually nearly spherical, and have fairly thick shells. Each nut is enclosed in a husk that may be anywhere from moderately thick to very thin, and that splits open—rather later in the season than other hickories—to the middle or sometimes to the base.

A very large-fruited variety of the pignut grows along the coast in the southeastern states; it is distinguished by numerous resinous scales on its leaflets. In the Great Smoky Mountains the pignut has been found at elevations up to 4,850 feet. One of the commonest hickories, it produces wood of the very best quality.

## PECAN (*Carya illinoensis*)

In a wild state the pecan grows in the forests of the Mississippi Valley region northward to the lower Ohio Valley and extreme southwestern Wisconsin. Today the cultivated descendants of the wild tree are grown in orchards and dooryards over a much wider territory. Everyone is familiar with the delicately flavored, sweet-meated nuts, though many may have never seen the tree from which they come. The Indians, who made much use of the nuts of the wild pecan, believed the tree was a manifestation of the Great Spirit himself. Its name is derived from the Algonquin word *paccan.*

The world's first published notice of the pecan was written by Captain Alvar Núñez Cabeza de Vaca—the same Spanish explorer whose life was saved by the seeds of the pinyon pine. In 1533, during their wanderings across Texas after being shipwrecked, he and his companions were captured and enslaved by the Mariames Indians, who put the captives to work pounding pecans in gourds with wooden pestles and thus Cabeza de Vaca was introduced to the fine nuts of the pecan tree.

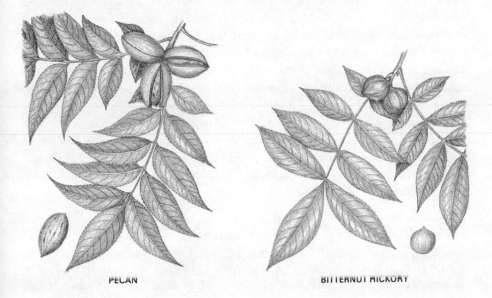

PECAN                                          BITTERNUT HICKORY

Largest of all the hickories, the pecan grows to a height of 100 to 140 feet, with a trunk from 2 to 4 feet in diameter. Exceptionally large pecan trees in the virgin forest attained heights up to 180 feet, with trunks as much as 6 feet in diameter. According to the American Forestry Association, the present champion is a tree in Louisiana's Assumption Parish with a height of 135 feet, a limb spread of 145 feet, and a trunk measuring 21 feet 4 inches in circumference at 4½ feet above the ground.

The leaves of the pecan range from 12 to 20 inches in length and are divided into from eleven to seventeen lance-shaped or slightly sickle-shaped leaflets. The reddish-brown nuts are oblong, with a point at one end, and are from 1 to 2 inches long. They are enclosed by a thin four-winged husk that splits into four sections. Nuts even of wild pecan trees have a much thinner bony shell than those of most hickories. Improved cultivated varieties commonly have shells so thin that they are called "paper-shell pecans."

The wood of the pecan is similar to that of other hickories. Hard, strong, heavy, and tough, it is used in making furniture, flooring, tool handles, boxes, and crates. It is an excellent fuel wood, and like the wood of other hickories it is used extensively for smoking meats.

Besides producing delicious nuts, the pecan makes a very handsome shade tree. A famous old pecan tree stands in the well-kept yard of Sam Houston's old home at Huntsville, Texas. Beneath this tree the General smoked the peace pipe with his Indian friends, and with his "paleface" comrades planned many a political campaign. It was the last wish of Governor Hogg of Texas that "no monument of stone or marble" be placed at his grave, but rather "at my head a pecan tree and at my feet an old-fashioned walnut; and when these trees shall bear, let the pecans and the walnuts be given out among the plains people of Texas so that they may plant them and make Texas a land of trees."

The Governor's wish has been carried out. Each year since 1926, the nuts have been gathered and planted in nursery rows; and as soon as the young trees become large enough to transplant, they are dug up and distributed. And Texas has made the pecan her state tree. The scientific name *illinoensis* means "of Illinois."

## BITTERNUT HICKORY (*Carya cordiformis*)

Every country boy within its range knows that the nuts produced by the hickory with the bright-yellow buds are unfit to eat. Their kernels are like gall, so intensely bitter that even squirrels won't touch them if they can find anything else. So the ground beneath a bitternut hickory is often littered with nuts, some perhaps having lain there for years.

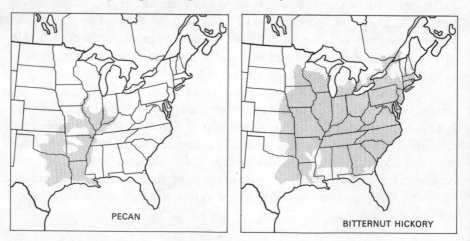

PECAN

BITTERNUT HICKORY

The bitternut has a wide range, extending from New Hampshire westward through southern Quebec to Minnesota, and southward to northwestern Florida and eastern Texas. It is the only member of the pecan-hickory group found in the Northeast, and it is the common hickory of the Missouri Valley in Kansas, Nebraska, and Iowa. Although it is most often found in the bottomlands and along streams, it may also occur far up the slopes of the mountains. In the Great Smokies, and probably elsewhere in the southern Appalachians, it is found up to altitudes of at least 3,000 feet. It reaches its greatest size, however, in the lower Ohio basin.

Commonly the bitternut hickory is 50 to 60 feet in height, with a trunk from 1 to 2 feet in diameter, but an occasional tree may attain a height of 100 feet or more, with a trunk 3 or 4 feet in diameter. The champion, according to the American Forestry Association, is a tree in Louisiana's West Feliciana Parish, which stands 171 feet high, with a trunk measuring 12 feet 6 inches in circumference at 4½ feet above the ground. That is perhaps an all-time record.

The leaves of the bitternut are from 6 to 10 inches long, divided into from seven to eleven lance-shaped, long-pointed leaflets with saw-toothed margins. They are dark yellowish-green on the upper surface, paler and sometimes a little downy underneath. The nuts are almost an inch long, spherical but slightly flattened, and pale reddish-brown. Each one is enclosed by a thin husk, which is four-winged above the middle and liberally sprinkled with tiny yellow dots. It splits into four parts to about the middle when the nuts ripen, usually in October.

Although the wood of the bitternut is similar in many ways to that of the other hickories—and is generally used for the same purposes—it is somewhat inferior to that of the shagbark and other so-called "true" hickories. On the other hand, the bitternut grows more rapidly than most of the other hickories and its wood is sufficiently valued that foresters grant it a place in forest management.

The scientific name *cordiformis,* which means "heart-shaped," perhaps refers to the fruits but is not particularly appropriate.

# BIRCH FAMILY

❧　ALL winter long, catkins of stamen-bearing flowers are visible on the branchlets of a birch. During the warm days of early spring these catkins elongate rapidly and sway in the winds, showering their light and dusty pollen so it may be carried to the pistil-bearing flowers. The latter are clustered in much smaller catkins, barely half an inch long, which emerge from ordinary-looking buds on the same branchlets, along with a pair of tiny leaves.

Later in the summer or in early fall, the catkins of the pistil-bearing flowers mature as conelike structures, within which are tiny seedlike fruits with pairs of side wings. At maturity the birch "cones" break up, sending earthward a shower of tiny winged fruits and thin three-lobed bracts which often have the shape of miniature fleurs-de-lis.

It is easy to tell a birch from other trees by the peculiar arrangement of the leaves. On twigs grown during the latest season, they appear alternately; but on those of the previous year, they are paired in short spurlike shoots. The smooth bark of the younger trunks and branches is marked with conspicuous horizontal rows of lenticels.

About forty species of birch are found throughout the Northern Hemisphere, and about fifteen of these grow in North America. Not all birches grow to tree size. Some that are native to the tundra of the far north, and to alpine mountain summits, are shrubs a mere few inches to a few feet tall. In addition to the native tree birches, the European white birch (*Betula pendula*), with its white-barked trunk and its gracefully drooping branches, is frequently planted as an ornamental tree in the cooler parts of the continent.

Along with the true birches, the birch family also includes the alders and hazelnuts, the American hornbeam or blue beech (*Carpinus caroliniana*), and the American hop hornbeam (*Ostrya virginiana*).

## YELLOW BIRCH (*Betula alleghaniensis*)

An outstanding feature of the yellow birch is its lustrous amber-yellow to silvery-gray bark, which peels horizontally into thin, papery, curled strips, giving the trunk a rather ragged appearance. On the trunks of very old trees the bark becomes broken into reddish-brown plates, but the younger limbs still carry this distinctively curled bark.

Yellow birches grow in cool, moist forests from Newfoundland and Nova Scotia west to Minnesota, around the southern end of the Great Lakes, and down along the Appalachians into northern Georgia. In the North the yellow birch is commonly associated with the sugar maple and the beech in what plant ecologists and foresters call "beech-birch-maple climax forest." Often, too, it keeps company with such conifers as hemlock, white pine, and spruce. Southward the yellow birch is common in the mountains, usually at elevations between 3,500 and 6,500 feet.

Average-sized yellow birches are between 60 and 70 feet in height, with a trunk from 1 to 2 feet in diameter, but under the most favorable conditions a tree may occasionally reach a height of 100 feet and have a trunk diameter of 3 or 4 feet. A champion, according to the American Forestry Association, grows in the Greenbrier area of the Great Smoky Mountains National Park. It is 90 feet in height and its trunk at 4½ feet above ground measures 14 feet 1 inch in circumference. Many other yellow birches in the park have trunks over 10 feet in circumference.

If you should happen to be traveling along the Blue Ridge Parkway through western North Carolina, be sure to stop at the overlook at Milepost 363.6—the one that affords a view of Graybeard Mountain. The overlook here rests along the flat of a high mountain "bench," and all about it is a brush-like forest of trees that have been stunted and twisted by the wind. Most of these trees are yellow birches, beeches, and yellow buckeyes. None is more than a few feet high, though they are quite old. In the sheltered coves farther down the slopes of these mountains, trees of the same kinds grow to be giants.

Like the hemlocks, yellow birches often begin to grow on top of mossy boulders or rotting stumps and logs. Eventually they send their roots down around the rocks or stumps and into the leaf mold and soil. In time many of the stumps or logs on which they have started to grow completely rot away, and the tree is left standing on what look like props or stilts.

From a commercial standpoint the yellow birch is the most important of all American birches. Its light-reddish-brown heartwood is heavy, hard, and strong, and has a fine, uniform texture. It is used for furniture, flooring, woodenware, interior finish, veneer, baskets, boxes, and crates. Another important use is for making charcoal and chemicals by distillation, and yellow birch wood is excellent for fuel.

*Betula* is the classical Latin name for a birch tree, and *alleghaniensis* means "of the Allegheny Mountains."

## BLACK BIRCH (*Betula lenta*)

The bark on the trunk of a young black birch tree—and on the slender, lithe branches of an older one—is smooth, shiny, dark reddish-brown to nearly black, and streaked with pale, horizontal, corky lines. It so closely resembles the bark of a cherry tree that the black birch is often called the cherry birch. Another feature is the marked wintergreen odor and taste of its slender reddish-brown twigs, a characteristic that has earned it still another name, that of sweet birch. The appearance of the bark and the wintergreen odor and taste readily distinguish a black birch from other trees. On the trunks of older trees the bark becomes a dark brownish-black and is broken into rather large scaly plates. The scientific name *lenta* means "flexible," and refers to the twigs.

Black birches grow in rich upland forests from southern Maine westward through New York to eastern Ohio and southward to Delaware, as well as along the Appalachians to the northern portions of Georgia and Alabama. The tree is commonly associated with various northern hardwood trees, white pines, and hemlocks. In rocky places it may be found side by side with the yellow birch, though it usually grows at lower elevations. In the southern Appalachians the black birch may be found at elevations of nearly 1,000 feet, and it may also ascend to the higher mountain peaks to mingle with the red spruce and the Fraser fir.

Ordinarily the black birch is a tree 50 to 60 feet in height, with a trunk between 1 and 2 feet in diameter. It usually attains its greatest size on the western slopes of the Appalachians in eastern Kentucky and Tennessee, where it may reach a height of about 80 feet and a trunk diameter of as much as 5 feet. According to the American Forestry Association, the champion black birch is a tree growing near New Boston, New Hampshire. It is 90 feet in height and has a limb spread of 64 feet, and a trunk measuring 14 feet 1 inch at 4½ feet above the ground. Young trees have a pyramidal crown which later becomes round-topped and relatively open, but is nevertheless very graceful.

The wood of the black birch is essentially like that of the yellow birch and is used for the same purposes. In fact, lumbermen make no distinction between the two, but market both simply as "birch" lumber. The flavor of the aromatic wintergreenlike oil from the twigs and inner bark is indistinguishable from that of the little teaberry or mountain tea—chemically known as methyl salicylate, and long used to relieve the pain of arthritis and rheumatism, as well as to flavor candies and chewing gum—and for years the greater part of the commercial product by the latter name was actually distilled from the twigs and bark of the black birch. Today it is nearly all made synthetically from wood alcohol and salicylic acid.

## RED BIRCH (*Betula nigra*)

The river birch, as the red birch is often called, is aptly named. It grows along practically every river and lesser stream from northern Florida west to eastern Texas, as well as north to Massachusetts and southern New Hampshire, southern Ohio, southern Wisconsin, and southeastern Minnesota. Throughout the lowlands of the southeastern states it is one of the most abundant and familiar trees, but it rarely follows the streams far enough into the mountains to meet its kin, the black and yellow birches.

There should be no trouble in recognizing the red birch, even at a considerable distance. The salmon-pink or cinnamon-colored bark peels off in ragged, papery-thin scales from a trunk that is usually short, dividing near the base into a few ascending limbs; these end in many branches and branchlets to form a rather open and irregular crown. Commonly the tree attains a height of 70 to 80 feet, with a trunk between 2 and 3 feet in diameter, but in the lower Mississippi Valley it frequently becomes 100 feet high, with trunk diameters of as much as 5 feet. The American Forestry Association's champion, however, is a tree near Odenton, Maryland, which has a height of 98 feet, a branch spread of 72 feet, and a trunk measuring 12 feet 4 inches in circumference at 4½ feet from the ground.

Like those of other birches, the flowers appear in the early spring before the leaves; but it is the only native birch whose conelike fruits mature in the late spring or early summer. Its fruiting coincides with the time of the year when the high waters are receding, leaving exposed large areas of silty mud in the stream bottoms—the best possible places for the little wind-borne seeds to germinate. The red birch seems to be most at home in bottomlands that are periodically flooded, and there it keeps company with such trees as the sycamore, American elm, eastern cottonwood, sweetgum, red and silver maples, and various willows.

Although the red birch ranks rather low in importance as a timber tree, it does have its merits. The wood is sometimes used for making cheap furni-

YELLOW BIRCH

YELLOW BIRCH

BLACK BIRCH

BLACK BIRCH

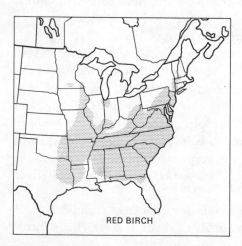

RED BIRCH

RED BIRCH

**PAPER BIRCH**

PAPER BIRCH

**GRAY BIRCH**

GRAY BIRCH

**RED ALDER**

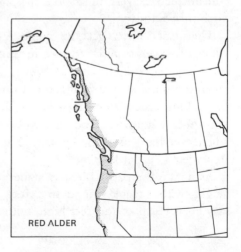

RED ALDER

ture, shoe lasts, wagon hubs, and various small turned articles. It finds a limited use even now in making hoops for peach baskets, and in bygone days it was much used in the hoops of rice casks. The tree renders a valuable service in helping to control the erosion of stream banks, a service much greater than is often realized. Red birches also make fine ornamental trees and are often planted in city parks and home grounds, including some of the finest estates. In the Pacific Northwest it is occasionally used as a street tree.

The scientific name *nigra,* which Linnaeus gave to this tree, is hardly appropriate, since there is nothing at all black about it.

## PAPER BIRCH (*Betula papyrifera*)

The white-barked trunks of paper birches gleam in forests stretching across Canada from the Atlantic westward into British Columbia, and into the state of Alaska. They grow southward through New England and northern Pennsylvania, around the Great Lakes, and westward through South Dakota to eastern Washington and northeastern Oregon. No other American birch has so wide a natural range. There are paper birches, too, on the summit of North Carolina's Mount Mitchell—the highest mountain peak east of the Mississippi River—hundreds of miles from others of their kind. During the Ice Age, when glaciers covered most of the land the paper birch now occupies, it undoubtedly grew in forests far south of its present range. The trees still remaining on Mount Mitchell are relics left stranded there after the chief range of the birches shifted northward in the wake of the retreating ice. They have persisted on the mountain summit because the climate there is very much like that of the north country where the paper birch thrives today.

The paper birch gets its name from its chalky-to-creamy-white bark, which separates from the trunks in thin, papery layers, exposing the orange-colored inner bark. Birch bark was long used by northern Indian tribes for making canoes, as a covering for dwellings, and in utensils and receptacles for storing food. Woodsmen know that the bark is very inflammable, but also quite waterproof, and therefore excellent for starting a campfire even when everything is dripping wet. The scientific name *papyrifera* appropriately means "paper-bearing."

As a rule the paper birch is a medium-sized tree from 50 to 70 feet in height, with a trunk from 1 to 2 feet in diameter. Occasionally a specimen may be as much as 120 feet high, with a trunk diameter of 3 to 4 feet. One at Lake Leelanau in Michigan is the current champion listed by the American Forestry Association. It is 96 feet tall, with a branch spread of 93 feet, and its trunk at 4½ feet above the ground measures 10 feet 11 inches in circumference. Although it grows rapidly, the paper birch rarely attains an age of more than eighty years. The known maximum age attained by a tree of the species is 140 years. The bark at the base of the trunk of an old tree becomes nearly black and is deeply furrowed.

In the forest paper birches usually occur as scattered trees, most commonly about lakes or along streams. They are often associated with the spruces and with the balsam fir, or with other hardwoods or conifers. The paper birch seeds abundantly in recently burned-over areas; in such places it frequently forms nearly pure stands, or mingles with the quaking aspen.

From a strictly commercial point of view, the paper birch is more useful as a source of pulpwood than as lumber. Its wood, however, is often used to make such things as toothpicks, spools, clothespins, shoe lasts, and various small turned articles. Within its natural range it has often been planted as an ornamental tree, although it has seldom been grown with much success beyond those boundaries.

## GRAY BIRCH (*Betula populifolia*)

From northeastern Pennsylvania northward through eastern New York and New England to Nova Scotia, the gray birch is one of the most common and conspicuous of trees. This is the little birch whose white-barked trunks so often grow in clumps, and are marked with triangular black patches beneath every branch. Within its range it is abundant in abandoned fields and in tracts of burned-over forest land. It is often called poverty birch or old-field birch because it grows so profusely on the most sterile and barren soils. Indeed, in the hard-coal region of Pennsylvania, it often grows abundantly on piles of culm, or coal refuse. Nevertheless, its white trunks and graceful branches and its light and delicate foliage make it one of our most beautiful trees.

Rarely does the gray birch attain a height of more than 20 to 30 feet, or have a trunk more than 6 to 10 inches in diameter; but on exceptionally favorable sites it has been known to grow as high as 40 feet, with a trunk diameter up to a foot and a half. It is often planted as an ornamental tree, and in a cultivated state it may reach a somewhat larger size. The American Forestry Association records a champion from the vicinity of Clarksville,

Maryland, which is 60 feet high, with a branch spread of 51 feet and a trunk circumference of 7 feet 3 inches at 4½ feet above the ground.

The scientific name *populifolia* means "poplar-leaved," and indeed the long-stalked leaves of the gray birch do flutter in the slightest breeze like those of an aspen. Measuring from 2 to 3 inches long, they are quite triangular in shape, with long tapering points at the tips. Their upper surfaces are a shiny dark green and they are paler beneath, with sharply double-toothed margins. Like the leaves of other birches, they turn golden-yellow in the fall.

Although the gray birch never reaches a sufficient size to become a valuable timber tree, its wood is sometimes used to make things such as toothpicks, spools, and other small turned articles; and it is excellent for fuel.

## RED ALDER (*Alnus rubra*)

It is quite natural to think of alders as large shrubs which commonly grow along streams and in swampy places, and over most of their range the eastern alders do just that. Nevertheless, even they sometimes grow to be respectable-sized trees. A common alder (*Alnus serrulata*) near Shreve, Wayne County, Ohio, is 40 feet tall and has a trunk that measures 1 foot 5 inches in circumference. In Ottawa County, Michigan, a speckled alder (*Alnus rugosa*) is 50 feet high, with a trunk 2 feet 6 inches in circumference. And in Rock Creek Park, Washington, D.C., a seaside alder (*Alnus maritima*) is 78 feet in height and has a trunk that measures 3 feet 5½ inches in circumference at 4½ feet above the ground. Even so, most Easterners are surprised when they learn that the most important hardwood timber tree of the Pacific Northwest is not an oak or a maple but a alder.

That tree is the red alder, the greatest of all American alders, and it grows along the Pacific coast from southeastern Alaska all the way down into southern California. Although it never attains the massive proportions of the conifers with which it is commonly associated, it does become quite large. Red alders are often between 80 and 100 feet in height, with a trunk from 1 to 3 feet in diameter. The American Forestry Association's present champion is one in Folk County, Oregon, which is 92 feet tall and has a trunk 13 feet 9 inches in circumference at 4½ feet above the ground. Another is reported along Redwood Creek, California, as being 126 feet in height.

In the forest the tree develops a slightly tapered bole, which is clear of branches for some distance from the ground and has a narrow, domelike crown. Open-grown red alders have broadly cone-shaped crowns which often extend nearly to the ground. The tree grows quite rapidly, often producing saw logs within thirty-five to fifty years. Commercial lumber made of the alder comes chiefly from Oregon and Washington. It is used principally in making furniture, but also for sashes, doors, and other millwork.

Like all other alders, the red alder bears two kinds of flowers, which are formed on the branchlets during the summer growing season; but as in most alders they remain on the branchlets all winter, ready to bloom in the spring before the new leaves appear. The stamen-bearing flowers are clustered in large catkins which in spring become elongated and shake out their dusty wind-borne pollen. The pistil-bearing catkins which are much smaller, develop into woody conelike structures that bear little, seedlike, winged fruits. In summer the red alder has typically oval-shaped leaves with irregularly toothed edges; and in winter its twigs may be distinguished by their rather large stalked buds sheathed with two or three hairy, red scales. The young trunks have mottled pale-gray or bluish-gray bark, sometimes covered with warty outgrowths. On older trees the bark becomes broken into large, flat, and irregular plates.

Red alders are never found more than fifty miles inland from the Pacific or at altitudes above 2,500 feet. Like the aspen, this is one of the first trees to invade clearings or burned-over areas; and the forest it forms is but a temporary one. After the alders have built up the soil, and have enriched it with nitrogen compounds formed by bacteria that live in little nodules on their roots, they are eventually succeeded by trees such as the Douglas fir, western hemlock, and Sitka spruce.

*Alnus* is the classical Latin name for an alder, and *rubra,* meaning "red," refers to the sapwood of this tree, which turns reddish when freshly cut.

# BEECH FAMILY

## AMERICAN BEECH (*Fagus grandifolia*)

❧    IN the forests of eastern North America, one of the most common and distinctive trees is the American beech. Even at a distance it may be recognized by the smooth, close-fitting, smoky-gray bark of its trunk and branches. No other native tree offers so tempting a place for carving initials and dates; and only trees growing in the most out-of-the-way and inaccessible places are apt to escape the attention of pocketknife artists. Perhaps the most famous inscription ever carved on the trunk of a beech was on a tree that for many years stood in the woods of Washington County in Tennessee. It read:

D. Boon cilled A BAR On Tree
in THE YEar 1760

More than one hundred years later the letters were still quite plain, and the scars, though not the actual words, were still visible when the tree finally fell in 1916.

The beech grows in woodlands from Nova Scotia and southern Ontario southward into northern Florida and eastern Texas. Although it does best on deep, rich, and well-drained soils, it is found in almost any soil where the surface layer does not dry out too quickly. In the open it develops a short, stocky trunk and a low, wide-spreading crown. In the forest the trunk grows straight and tall, and remains clear of branches some distance above the ground. Ordinarily the beech is a tree from 70 to 80 feet tall, with a trunk 2 or 3 feet in diameter; but occasionally one may grow much larger. One at Saugatuck, Michigan, 91 feet in height with a trunk 18 feet 5 inches in circumference at breast height, is an American Forestry Association champion. Another, in Louisiana's West Feliciana Parish, is 126 feet tall and has a circumference of 12 feet 10 inches.

Aside from its distinctive bark, a beech may be known in winter by its brown, lustrous, somewhat zig-zag twigs with their long, slender, sharply pointed light-brown buds. In summer the bright-green leaves, with parallel straight veins running into the sharp and slightly curved marginal teeth, are distinctive. The leaves turn yellow or a rich bronze in the fall. Sometimes they linger well into the winter, eventually fading to a very pale tan about the color of parchment. In spring, when the new leaves are about half-grown, little, ball-shaped, yellowish-green clusters of stamen-bearing flowers hang from the branchlets on threadlike stalks. They are quite conspicuous,

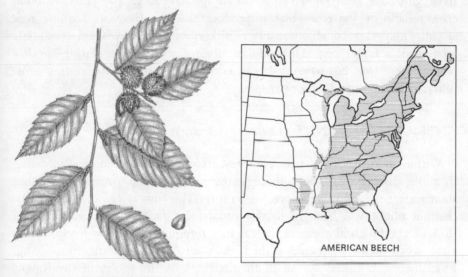

AMERICAN BEECH

AMERICAN BEECH

but the pistil-bearing flowers—which by fall develop into little burs enclosing nuts—are not so easily seen. Within each down-lined bur there may be two or three small, three-sided, lustrous brown, sweet-meated nuts. From them the Indians pressed an oil that would keep for a long time without becoming rancid, and that was highly prized for cooking. *Fagus,* the classical Latin name of the beech tree, is derived from a Greek word meaning "to eat," and refers to the edible quality of beechnuts. The name *grandifolia* means "large-leaved."

Over most of its range the American beech is not dependable as a source of food for forest wildlife, since years often pass between good fruiting years.

Also, for some unknown reason, better crops and larger nuts are produced in the northern part of its range than elsewhere.

The beech produces a light-reddish-brown wood which is heavy, hard, strong, and difficult to split. It is excellent for flooring, furniture, handles, laundry appliances, and various articles of woodenware. Since it has almost no perceptible taste or odor, beech wood is often used to make barrels, boxes, and other containers for foods. Woodsmen rate it as one of the very best fuel woods. It burns with a clean, hot flame and leaves a bed of long-lasting, glowing coals.

The American beech makes a fine shade tree, but it is not often planted for this purpose, mainly because it grows so slowly. But beeches are long-lived, and have been known to attain an age of 300 to 400 years. Another characteristic of the tree—that it produces suckers from its shallow root system—may also be objectionable. Thickets of small trees are commonly seen about a larger one. They seldom attain any great size during the life of the parent tree, but when it dies or is cut down, these sprouts often grow into trees that eventually take its place.

## AMERICAN CHESTNUT (*Castanea dentata*)

Within the memory of man no forest tragedy has been more devastating than the disease that swept through the ranks of the American chestnut shortly after the turn of the present century. The fungus responsible for the chestnut blight was brought to this country by accident, presumably on a stock of the Oriental chestnut. It was first recognized in New York City in 1904, when the chestnut trees at the New York Zoological Park began dying. From there the disease spread in all directions, as the spores of the fungus were carried by the winds from tree to tree. Steadily it spread northward, westward, and southward. Twenty years later it reached the southern Appalachians, and the splendid American chestnut was doomed.

Little more than half a century ago, the American chestnut flourished in forests that stretched from southern Maine westward to southern Michigan, and southward into northern Georgia, Alabama, and Mississippi. It was a grand tree and one of the most useful that ever grew in any forest. Not only was the chestnut an excellent timber tree, but its bark was a rich source of tannin, and in fall the sweet nuts regularly provided food for the wildlife of the forest. As a shade tree it had few peers, for in the open it developed a broadly spreading crown of exceptional beauty.

Although today chestnuts are still to be seen in the forest, they stand ghostlike and naked, their great trunks striped of bark, like the bleaching bones of giants. The sprouts that still continue to come from their roots and stumps often grow to be 10 or 15 feet tall, and some now and then blossom and even bear a few nuts; but invariably they are killed, for the deadly spores of the fungus still lurk in the old stumps and snags. For years it was hoped that somewhere at least a few of the trees might have developed an immunity to the disease. That hope now seems a forlorn one, yet even so it still lives on.

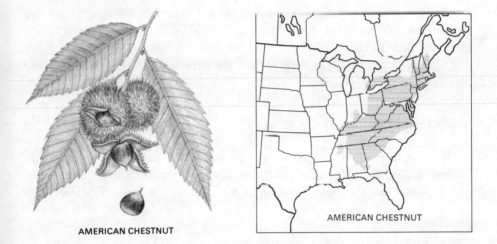

AMERICAN CHESTNUT

AMERICAN CHESTNUT

The American chestnut was one of the largest hardwood trees in the eastern forests. It commonly grew to a height of 70 to 90 feet, with a trunk from 3 to 4 feet in diameter, but much larger trees were not unusual. The species attained its greatest size in the mountains of western North Carolina and eastern Tennessee. Forester Joseph S. Illick reported that a chestnut tree in Francis Cove, near Waynesville, North Carolina, had a trunk diameter of 17 feet, and A. J. Sharp measured the ankle-high stump of one in the Greenbrier section of the Great Smoky Mountains National Park that was "13 feet the long way across."

Chestnut trees could be depended upon to bear a good crop of nuts almost every year, since they did not bloom until June or July and thus escaped possible injury by late frosts. An American chestnut covered with creamy-white blossoms was a spectacular sight. The individual flowers were not large, but the stamen-bearing ones were crowded in long, narrow, candlelike clusters. In the fall, usually after the first heavy frost, the prickly burs split open and the flattened, bright-brown nuts tumbled to the ground. Farm and city dwellers alike flocked to the woods to gather the sweet-meated nuts, and large quantities were sold in the markets; yet plenty were always left over for the bears, deer, squirrels, wild turkeys, and other wild birds and mammals.

The wood of the American chestnut is reddish-brown in color, rather coarse in texture, moderately light and hard, and very resistant to decay. It was used for general construction, furniture, boxes and crates, posts and poles. Today, of course, what supply remains has come from blight-killed trees. Throughout the Appalachians, chestnut was the favorite wood for making the old-time rail fences that are familiar today to all who travel along the Blue Ridge Parkway.

*Castanea* is the classical Latin name for the chestnut tree, and *dentata,* meaning "toothed," refers to the leaf margins.

## TANOAK (*Lithocarpus densiflorus*)

Of about a hundred species of tanoaks known to science, only one grows in the New World. All of the others are found in southern and eastern Asia and in Malaysia. The North American tanoak may be found from western

TANOAK

TANOAK

Oregon southward along the coast ranges to the Santa Ynez Mountains of southern California, and in the Sierra Nevada.

Tanoaks are unusual evergreen trees, with characteristics of both oaks and chestnuts. Their flowers resemble those of the chestnut, in that the stamen-bearing catkins stand erect like white candles; the few pistil-bearing flowers are at the bases of these spikes. The fruits of the tanoaks are acorns, which are seated in cups like those of the true oaks, but the loose and bristly scales give them the look of burs. In fact, the tanoaks seem to be a connecting link between oaks and chestnuts.

The trunk of our tanoak—or tan-bark oak, as it is often called—has a smooth appearance and is pale brown, tinged with red and often showing grayish areas. The bark on young trunks and on the branches of older trees is smooth and unbroken, but on older trunks it is thick and furrowed with deep but narrow seams, which cut it into very wide, squarish plates. The young twigs at first are densely woolly, but after the first year the wool disappears and the branchlets become dark reddish-brown. The oblong leaves are leathery, pale-green and shiny above, and measure 3 to 5 inches long. Their lower surfaces are at first densely coated with reddish-brown hairs but later become smooth or nearly so, and develop a bluish-white color. The leaves resemble those of chestnuts in that the main veins run from the midrib into the marginal teeth.

Most often the tanoak is a tree 50 to 70 feet, or rarely 90 to 150 feet in height, with a trunk usually from 1 to 2, but sometimes 3 to 5, feet in diameter. The American Forestry Association records as the present champion a tree near Cazedero in Sonoma County, California. It has a height of 80 feet with a branch spread of 84 feet, and its trunk is 24 feet 1 inch in circumference at 4½ feet above the ground. As a rule the tanoak attains its greatest size in the redwood belt of California; in other places it may be little more than a large shrub.

Today the tanoak has relatively little economic importance. In former years it was extensively cut for its tannin-rich bark. The wood is used for mine timbers and as fuel, and to a very limited extent in making furniture. Although the kernels of its acorns are intensely bitter, some of the California Indians used them for food after leaching them to remove the bitter tannin. The tanoak makes a very attractive ornamental tree when planted within or near its range, but elsewhere it has not been very successful.

*Lithocarpus* comes from the Greek words for "stone" and "fruit"—a reference to the hard acorns—and *densiflorus* means "densely flowered."

# The Oaks

Oaks are among the world's best-known and most useful trees. They are widely distributed throughout the forests of the Northern Hemisphere, and at high mountain elevations they are found well into the tropical regions of the world. Since some seventy-five- or eighty-different species are found in North America north of Mexico, getting acquainted with them all—or even with the tree-sized ones—is a pretty big job. To complicate matters further, the various species often cross with one another. Although it is quite easy to recognize any one of them as an oak by the acorns that are their characteristic fruit, it is often difficult to distinguish one kind of oak from another.

We are so accustomed to thinking of oaks as large and sturdy trees that they have become more or less a symbol of rugged strength and durability. The Druids, among other ancient peoples, held the massive oak to be a sacred tree, and ceremoniously gathered the mistletoe which often grows as a parasite on its branches. Some oaks are indeed trees of noble stature, but not all of them. Many are mere shrubs, and some never grow more than a few feet high.

The flowers of oaks appear in the early spring, just as the new leafy shoots are coming out of their buds. Those that bear the stamens are the most noticeable, yet few people would take even them for flowers. They are strung along slender, dangling threads, in clusters that emerge from buds on the previous year's twigs. Each tiny flower has a four- to seven-lobed calyx and from six to, rarely, as many as twelve stamens. As the dry, powdery pollen is shaken into the air, it covers everything about the trees with what looks like a fine, yellowish dust, much to the dismay of those who happen to be allergic to it.

To find the pistil-bearing flowers—those that will grow into acorns after the process of fertilization—it is necessary to look a little more closely. Borne on the new leafy shoots, in the axils of some of the new leaves, they do not look very much like flowers either. Each one is just a pistil, surrounded by a six-lobed calyx and partly enclosed by a cluster of minute scales. If all goes well, it will develop into an acorn seated in a cup that is scaly on the outside.

Oaks are generally divided into two groups, the white oaks and the red oaks. The former produce acorns in a single growing season, and as a rule the kernels are rather sweet, since they contain little of the bitter tannin. In those white oaks that have toothed or lobed leaves, the identations are more or less rounded. Members of the red-oak group usually require two seasons to mature their acorns, and the kernels are usually quite bitter to the taste. In those with lobed leaves, each of the lobes or teeth, if any are present, is tipped with a bristle. Red oaks with unlobed leaves generally have a little bristle at the tip of each leaf.

Oaks have served man in many ways. Many of them are important timber trees, or are highly prized as shade trees. Cork is obtained from the thick bark of the cork oak of southern Europe. Tannin for making hides into leather is derived from the bark of many others; and ink is made from the leaf galls produced by tiny insects on the leaves of some Old World oaks. Acorns are an important source of food for wildlife, and they have also been used as food for domesticated animals and man. American Indians once ground them into meal—as in some places they still do—after first removing the bitter tannin by washing them in running or boiling water. Some Pacific coast tribes relied on acorns to such an extent that they were known as the "acorn eaters."

*Quercus* is the classical Latin name of the oaks. The oaks make up the largest group or genus of the beech family, which also includes the beeches and the chestnuts.

## WHITE OAK (*Quercus alba*)

From Central Maine through southern Ontario to Minnesota, and southward into northern Florida and almost to the Gulf coast, the white oak is one of the most familiar trees. It grows in many kinds of soil, very often including the drier hilltops, but it reaches its best development where soils are deep and moist but well-drained. It becomes a large tree, often 80 to 100 feet in height, with a trunk 3 to 4 feet in diameter, and has been known to attain a height of about 150 feet with trunk diameters up to about 8 feet. In the open the white oak develops a short but stocky trunk, which divides into great wide-spreading branches, but in the forest the trunks grow straight and tall and the trees have rather small and narrow crowns.

The white oak takes both its common name and the scientific name of *alba,* meaning "white," from the light-ashy-gray color of its bark. Its leaves are from 5 to 9 inches long, and have from seven to nine fingerlike lobes, which are irregularly rounded at the tip. They are a bright green on the upper surface, pale or slightly whitened and smooth beneath. In fall they turn color, ranging from purplish-red to russet; and some tawny-brown leaves often linger on the branches well into the winter.

The white oak's pale-chestnut-brown acorns are often ¾ inch long and are seated in the bowl-shaped cups covered with warty scales. Since they contain little of the bitter tannin present in the acorns of many oaks, they are greedily eaten by squirrels, deer, wild turkeys, jays, and many other birds and mammals. The Indians, too, often boiled them or ground them into meal for making bread—a practice that was followed by many white settlers in early days.

Throughout the tree's range, many great white oaks are centuries old. Maryland's Eastern Shore is noted for its grand old oak trees; one of the most famous is the Wye Mills Oak, which stands about nine miles from Easton. Its massive trunk has a circumference of 27 feet 9 inches at 4½ feet above the ground, and its branches have a spread of 165 feet. Its age has been estimated at about 450 years. In the Friends' Cemetery at Salem, New Jersey, stands another white oak which is nearly 90 feet tall and has a branch spread of 120 feet, with a trunk nearly 20 feet in circumference. This great tree is supposed to have been in its prime when the town of Salem was founded in 1675, and the Quaker John Fenwick, in the shade of the tree, made a treaty with the Indians that has never been broken. There are historic white oaks in other states, too. Among them is the Witness Tree, which stands before the Donegal Presbyterian Church in Lancaster County, Pennsylvania. Beneath its spreading branches the congregation swore allegiance to the infant Republic in June 1777. And there are many, many others.

Probably the largest white oak that ever grew in the United States formerly stood near the Trace Fork of Pigeon Creek in Mingo County, West Virginia. It is said to have been 145 feet tall and to have had a trunk circumference of about 30 feet at the base. Perkins Coville of the U.S. Forest Service estimated its volume at 20,000 board feet of lumber. This great tree, called the Mingo White Oak, died around 1938. Its age at that time was estimated to be 583 years.

At Athens, Georgia, is a white oak known as the Oak that Owns Itself. At the base of the tree is a stone bearing this inscription:

FOR AND IN CONSIDERATION
OF THE GREAT LOVE I BEAR
THIS TREE AND THE GREAT DE-
SIRE I HAVE FOR ITS PROTECTION
FOR ALL TIME, I CONVEY ENTIRE
POSSESSION OF ITSELF AND
ALL LAND WITHIN EIGHT FEET
OF THE TREE ON ALL SIDES.
WILLIAM H. JACKSON

**WHITE OAK**

WHITE OAK

**CALIFORNIA WHITE OAK**

CALIFORNIA
WHITE OAK

**OREGON WHITE OAK**

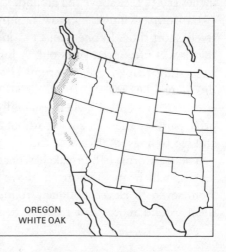

OREGON
WHITE OAK

The deed from which the inscription is taken is dated 1820, and is duly recorded in the office of the town clerk.

White oak wood is heavy, hard, strong, and moderately resistant to decay. It was the wood always chosen for old-time buckets, wash tubs, and kegs and barrels intended to hold liquids. Such containers are known as "tight cooperage." For "slack cooperage"—containers to be used for things other than liquids—almost any kind of wood might do. White oak was formerly employed wherever strength and durability were of utmost importance—for bridges and ships, the beams of barns, wagons and agricultural implements, and railroad ties. It was also good for fence posts and mine props, and its tannin-rich bark was always in demand at tanneries. Today, though it is still used for some of these purposes, it is prized most highly for things such as flooring, furniture, and fine cabinet work.

As a shade tree the white oak has always been highly esteemed. For both beauty and durability it has few rivals. Connecticut and Maryland have both chosen it as their state tree.

## CALIFORNIA WHITE OAK (*Quercus lobata*)

In its native habitat, the California white oak is often called the valley oak, since it is very largely restricted to valley sites in the western part of the state. It has the distinction of being the largest of Western oaks. Trees from 50 to 75 feet high are common, and some may be from 90 to 125 feet high, with trunks from 5 to 10 feet in diameter. The current champion listed by the American Forestry Association is a tree near Middletown in Lake County. It has a height of 125 feet and a trunk circumference of 27 feet 9 inches at 4½ feet above the ground.

California white oaks grow rapidly and attain a large size in a comparatively short time. In one tree, 21¼ inches in diameter, growth rings indicated that it was fifty-seven years old. A big California white oak often has a form suggesting that of the American elm, with wide-spreading limbs and long, drooping branches. It has made an excellent shade tree in California, but efforts to grow it elsewhere generally prove unsuccessful. Its wood is used principally as fuel. In some parts of its range the sweet acorns are gathered and fed to hogs in place of grain.

The California white oak has deciduous leaves, from 2½ to 4 inches in length, which are dark-green above and grayish-hairy beneath. They have from seven to eleven obliquely rounded lobes, and the depressions between them extend more than halfway to the midrib. The scientific name *lobata* refers to these leaves. The acorns, like those of other white oaks, mature in one season, and are sometimes produced in very large quantities. They are chestnut-brown in color, slender and pointed, from 1¼ to 2¼ inches long; and they are seated in deeply bowl-shaped, warty-scaled woolly cups for about a third of their length. On the trunk of a California white oak, the ashy-gray-to-brown bark is deeply furrowed and broken horizontally into thick plates.

## OREGON WHITE OAK (*Quercus garryana*)

Next to the California white oak, the Oregon white oak is the largest of its kind in the Pacific coast region. In many places it reaches between 50 and 90 feet in height, with a trunk from 2 to 5 feet in diameter. On high mountain slopes, however, it is a small, shrubby tree, and in exposed situations along the seacoast it is no more than a very low shrub. It is, nevertheless, the only timber oak of the northwest coast country. The champion, according to the American Forestry Association, is a tree near the Mendocino National Forest in California, with a height of 120 feet and a trunk that is 25 feet 6 inches in circumference at 4½ feet above the ground. The Oregon white oak is found from the tip of Vancouver Island southward into the Santa Cruz Mountains of California.

At its best the Oregon white oak is a massive and rugged-looking tree with a short trunk and a wide-spreading, round-topped crown. Its leaves are from 3 to 6 inches long, somewhat leathery, shiny dark-green above, paler and usually hairy beneath. They have from five to nine rather long, blunt-pointed lobes, the thickened edges of which often curl toward the underside. In winter, when the leaves are absent, the orange-red and downy twigs with their big rusty-brown buds are conspicuous. The light-brown, broad, rounded acorns are 1 to 1¼ inches long; and they are seated in shallow bowllike cups which have downy, loose-tipped scales. Like those of other white oaks, they mature in one season and have sweetish kernels.

The heavy, hard, strong, durable wood of the Oregon white oak is pale yellowish-brown in color. It is used for furniture, shipbuilding, general construction, agricultural implements, cabinet work, interior finish, and barrels, and as fuel.

This tree is often called the Garry oak. The name *garryana*, given by David Douglas in 1839 honors Nicholas Garry, a secretary of the Hudson's Bay Company, who aided Douglas in his botanical exploration of the Pacific Northwest.

## BUR OAK (*Quercus macrocarpa*)

The greatest bur oaks are often close rivals of the white oaks and the live oaks as the largest and most majestic of American oaks. In the open this tree develops a broadly round-topped crown with stout spreading limbs and often drooping branches, but in the forest the trunk grows straight and tall, and the tree has a smaller and more compact crown. Bur oaks commonly attain a height of 70 to 80 feet, with trunks 2 to 3 feet in diameter, but an occasional specimen may be as high as 170 feet and have a trunk diameter of 7 feet or more.

As a rule these trees attain their greatest size in the lower Ohio Valley, but truly big ones are sometimes found elsewhere within their range. Joseph S. Illick in his *Pennsylvania Trees* described a bur oak, which stood until 1924 in Huntingdon County, as having a trunk 39 feet 9 inches in circumference at the ground, and a breast-high diameter of almost 7 feet. The present champion recorded by the American Forestry Association is a tree at Algonac, St. Clair County, Michigan, which has a trunk 20 feet 9 inches in circumference at 4½ feet above ground, a height of 122 feet, and a branch spread of 107 feet.

Typically this oak is a tree of the bottomlands. It is commonly associated with such trees as pin and willow oaks, red and silver maples, American elm, sweet gum, and bald cypress. Although it grows most abundantly in the north-central United States, its range extends from New Brunswick and Maine west to southeastern Saskatchewan, and southward to Maryland, West Virginia, Tennessee, and eastern and central Texas. It forms the "oak openings" of the western Great Lakes region, and is the most common oak in the Prairie States.

Any oak that has conspicuous corky ridges or wings on its branchlets is quite certainly a bur oak. Its leaves have the peculiarity of being cut nearly to the midrib about the middle by opposing indentations. Above this cleft the leaf is broadest and shallowly lobed; below it, the depressions between the lobes are often quite deep. All summer the leaves are dark-green and rather shiny above, grayish to whitish and hairy beneath. In fall they turn dull yellow, then brown, and are promptly shed.

Still another distinctive feature of the bur oak is its acorns. They are big and sweet-meated, usually between 1 and 2 inches long, broadly egg-shaped, and enclosed for half or more of their length by deep cups with fringelike rims. From these "bur-like" cups came the common name of the bur oak, as well as another by which it is known in many places—mossycup oak. The scientific name *macrocarpa* means "large-fruited."

The wood of the bur oak is similar in most respects to that of the white oak, so much so that the lumbermen do not bother to make any distinction. The tree grows slowly, attaining maturity in 200 to 300 years; but it makes a most handsome and durable shade or street tree, and has been widely planted in shelterbelts on the Great Plains. Not only is it adaptable to a variety of soils and climates, but it also shows remarkable ability to withstand city conditions. Illinois has selected the bur oak as its state tree.

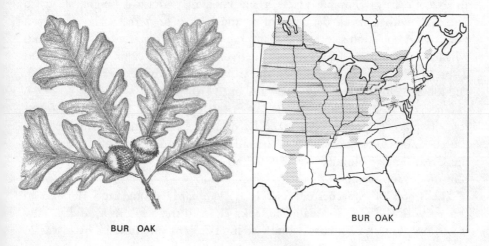

BUR OAK

BUR OAK

## CHESTNUT OAK (*Quercus prinus*)

A slight similarity in leaf shape gave the chestnut oak its common name. Aside from their narrowly oval shape, however, they are of a much firmer leathery texture, and the large scalloped teeth on their edges are blunt or rounded rather than sharply pointed. They are from 5 to 8 inches long and shiny dark-green above, with stout, yellow leaf stalks and yellow midribs. In fall they become a dull orange or light yellowish-brown before dropping from the tree.

The bark on the trunk of this oak is distinctive, too—almost black and deeply furrowed, with irregular sharp-topped ridges between the furrows. The brown, lustrous, narrowly oval-shaped acorns are from 1 to 1½ inches long, and are about half enclosed by the thin, deeply bowl-shaped, warty-scaled cups. Their sweetish white kernels are relished by deer, squirrels, bears, and many other wild creatures; but the oaks do not provide as dependable a food supply as the ill-fated chestnut once did.

The chestnut oak is found from southern Maine southwestward to southern Indiana and south to northern Georgia and Mississippi. Sometimes it is called the rock oak, since it is commonly found on the dry rocky ridges and slopes of the mountains. In the southern Appalachians it is one of the most common trees, growing to an elevation of about 4,000 feet; it is also quite common in the lower Hudson Valley of New York.

Although on many of the poorer sites the chestnut oak is small, it often grows to a height of 60 to 70 feet, with a trunk from 2 to 3 feet in diameter. In exceptionally favorable places a specimen may attain a height of up to 100 feet, with a trunk diameter of as much as 6 or 7 feet. The American Forestry Association's present champion is a tree at Easton, Maryland, which has a trunk 22 feet 3 inches in circumference, a height of 95 feet, and a spread of 108 feet. In the open the trunk usually divides near the ground, and the branches form a very broad and open crown.

Since the disappearance of the American chestnut as a dominant forest tree, its place has often been taken by oaks of various kinds. Among these the chestnut oak is prominent, especially in the southern Appalachians. In the Great Smoky Mountains it has led all other trees, accounting for 17 per cent of the replacement.

The wood of the chestnut oak is heavy, hard, strong, and durable in contact with the soil. In quality it ranks close to the white oak, and usually it is simply cut and sold as "white oak lumber." At one time its bark was in great demand at tanneries because of its very high tannin content. In some places these oaks, like the hemlocks, were felled and stripped of their bark, leaving the trunks in the woods to rot slowly away.

The scientific name *prinus* is derived from the classic Greek word for the European holm oak.

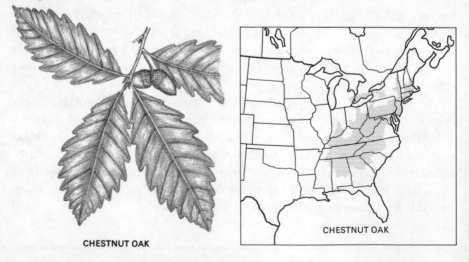

CHESTNUT OAK

CHESTNUT OAK

## LIVE OAK (*Quercus virginiana*)

Southward from Virginia's Dismal Swamp the traveler comes into the realm of the live oaks, and from there down the coast into Florida, and westward along the gulf coast to Texas, these majestic trees are seldom long out of sight. Their impressiveness is not in their height but rather in their massive trunks and in the immense spread of their gnarled branches, which are usually draped with the plant known as Spanish moss. Although the live oak is a native of this coastal country, it is also widely planted as a shade tree. In the old days, avenues of live oaks commonly lined the sandy roads leading to plantation houses. Today such avenues of oaks often lead nowhere, since many of the big plantation houses are gone, but they still recall the romance and the grandeur of the Old South. The scientific name *virginiana* means "of Virginia."

Live oaks attain a height of 40 to 80 feet, with a branch spread that is 100 to 150 feet or more. Their trunks are 3, rarely, as much as 8 feet in diameter, above a swollen and buttressed base. Not far above the ground, the trunk typically divides into from three to five immense, horizontal, wide-spreading branches to form a broad, dome-shaped crown. The American Forestry Association's champion is a tree growing near Hahnville, Louisiana. It is 78 feet high with a limb spread of 168 feet, and its great trunk measures 35 feet in circumference at 4½ feet above the ground.

The famous old oak at Middleton Gardens on the Ashley River, about seventeen miles north of Charleston, South Carolina, is another outstanding specimen. Its massive trunk has a circumference of 35 feet at 5 feet above the ground, and its branches form an almost perfect circle, giving a shade span at noon of 180 feet. Some estimates have placed the age of this tree as high as from five to seven centuries. Studies made by scientists in recent years,

LIVE OAK

LIVE OAK

however, tend to refute the great age claimed for many big live oaks. There is some doubt whether even the largest of those standing today are much more than 200 or 300 years old. On rich soils, the growth of the tree is surprisingly fast. In Georgia live oaks have attained a diameter of about 4½ feet in less than seventy years.

Throughout the coastal regions of the South there are many fine big live oaks, many with historical associations. At Hampton Plantation near Mc-Clellanville, South Carolina, one is known as the Washington Live Oak. Legend has it that while President Washington was a guest of the Pinckneys at the plantation in 1791, he overheard the mistress of the house order the gardener to cut down the large oak which obstructed the view from the new portico. The story goes that Washington, who was a great lover of trees, asked that the oak be spared. It was, and it still stands today.

The South's Living Christmas Tree is not a conifer but a magnificent live oak growing in Hilton Park at Wilmington, North Carolina. Its trunk has a circumference of about 15 feet, its height is 75 feet, and its branches have a spread of about 110 feet. Nature has adorned the tree with about five tons of Spanish moss, and each year at Christmas it is further decorated with 4,500 multicolored lights.

In the days of wooden ships, the live oak was used extensively in ship-building, especially for ships' knees. Its importance was so great that the United States Navy acquired several live-oak forests, the first on St. Catherines Island off the coast of Georgia—a state which has made the live oak its state tree. Live-oak timbers from St. Catherines went into the building of the U.S. frigate *Constitution,* the famous "Old Ironsides" which helped to drive the Barbary pirates from the seas.

Live oaks are so called because they do not shed their leaves in the fall as most other oaks do. Instead, the leaves remain green on the trees until spring, when they are shed after the new leaves appear—and thus the tree is an evergreen. The leaves are rather stiff and leathery in texture, shiny dark-green above, whitish-downy beneath, with edges that are usually smooth and slightly rolled. The dark-brown or almost black acorns are seated in deep cups, and usually two or more occur on each stalk. They mature in a single season.

Several species of live oak are found in the arid Southwest and in California. Many of them are mere shrubs or small trees, but occasionally they reach a considerable size. At Chiles Va Mey, Napa County, California, is a California life oak (*Quercus agrifolia*) 108 feet high, with a branch spread of 129 feet and a trunk circumference of 24 feet 10 inches. A canyon live oak

(*Quercus chrysolepis*) in the Angeles National Forest of California has a height of 70 feet, a branch spread of 130 feet, and a trunk 36 feet 3 inches in circumference. An interior live oak (*Quercus wislizenii*) near Sacramento, California, is 100 feet tall, with a limb spread of 100 feet and a trunk circumference of 20 feet.

## NORTHERN RED OAK (*Quercus rubra*)

The northern red oak is one of the largest and most widely distributed, and commercially the most valuable, of the red oak tribe. It grows in forests from Nova Scotia westward to Ontario and Minnesota, and southward in the uplands to northern Georgia, Mississippi, Arkansas, and Oklahoma. Occasionally it attains a height of 150 feet and a trunk diameter up to about 6 feet, but more commonly it is 70 to 90 feet high with a trunk between 2 and 3 feet in diameter. A champion reported by the American Forestry Association has a trunk 26 feet 4 inches at 4½ feet above the ground and a height of 78 feet. This tree grows at Ashford, Connecticut. Another at Conneaut, Ohio, has a height of 89 feet and a trunk circumference of 22 feet 10 inches.

Several features aid in distinguishing this oak. On larger trees the dark bark covering the trunk becomes broken into wide, flat-topped ridges which

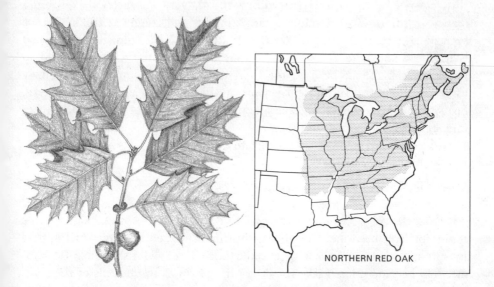

NORTHERN RED OAK

NORTHERN RED OAK

are silvery-grayish in color. The thin-textured leaves are a dull dark green above, and are smooth underneath except for occasional tufts of down along the midrib where the main veins branch off. The depressions between the seven to eleven bristle-tipped and sparingly bristle-toothed lobes extend no more than halfway to the midrib of the leaf. In fall the leaves usually turn anywhere from a deep red to bright orange. The acorns are larger than those of any other of the red oaks—often an inch or more long and almost as broad. Usually they have shallow saucerlike cups with smooth, close-fitting scales, but in one variety the cups are deeper and more bowl-shaped. The scientific name *rubra* means "red."

The northern red oak grows rapidly and does not attain the great age of the white oak. Few probably live longer than 200 to 300 years. Although relatively few are associated with tradition or historical events, a big red oak at Lloyd Neck, on the northern shore of Long Island, is still pointed out as the tree from which the American patriot Nathan Hale was hanged by the British on September 22, 1776. Another such tree shades the old Walker Tavern in Michigan, whose roof sheltered James Fenimore Cooper and other notables of early days. Here Cooper is said to have written *Oak Openings*. At the time of the rally for "Tippecanoe and Tyler Too," the top of the tree was thinned out so that a flag might be flown from a high place.

The northern red oak is outstanding as both a shade and a timber tree. In the open it is a beautiful tree with a broad, very symmetrical, spreading crown. In the forest it develops a tall, straight, and columnar trunk, free of branches for some distance above the ground. Its light-reddish-brown wood is hard but not quite as heavy and strong as that of the white oak, and so porous that it cannot be used for tight cooperage. As lumber it is widely used for flooring, furniture, general millwork, agricultural implements, boats, woodenware, handles, boxes, and crates. It also goes into railroad ties mine timbers, fenceposts, and fuel.

New Jersey has made this oak her state tree.

## SCARLET OAK (*Quercus coccinea*)

The scarlet oak's scientific name, *coccinea,* also means "scarlet," and the tree could not have been more appropriately named. When its leaves first appear in spring they are bright red, covered with loose whitish hairs. In summer they become smooth save for little tufts of down in the axils of the main veins on the lower surface, and above they become a lustrous bright green.

From three to six inches in length, they usually have seven long lobes which are bristle-tipped and sparingly bristle-toothed, and the indentations between the lobes go deep toward the midrib. In autumn the leaves of the scarlet oak end their days in a blaze of scarlet glory.

Like those other members of the red oak tribe, the scarlet oak's acorns do not mature until the autumn of the second year. They are one-half to three-quarters of an inch long, reddish-brown in color, and are seated in deep bowllike cups which have close-fitting, lustrous, reddish-brown scales. The kernels of the acorns are almost white and faintly bitter.

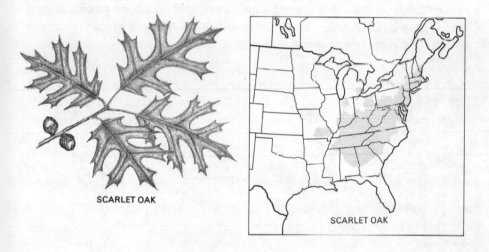

SCARLET OAK

SCARLET OAK

The scarlet oak is a tree of the uplands, usually found on dry and sandy or rocky soils. It grows from southern Maine west to Minnesota, and southward into northern Georgia and southeastern Arkansas, but is nowhere more abundant than in the Appalachian region. Usually a tree from 70 to 80 feet tall, with a trunk from 2 to 3 feet in diameter, it sometimes attains a height up to 100 feet with a trunk 4 feet in diameter. The American Forestry Association's current champion—a tree at Swarthmore, Pennsylvania—is 102 feet tall, with a branch spread of 110 feet. Its trunk has a circumference of 15 feet 9 inches at 4½ feet above the ground. Another tree, growing in the Smokemont campground area of the Great Smoky Mountains National Park, has a trunk 11 feet in circumference.

Scarlet oaks make excellent shade and ornamental trees, but as timber trees they are only second-rate. Their wood is generally regarded as inferior to that of the northern red oak, though such trees as are cut by lumbermen go to market as "red oak" lumber.

## PIN OAK (*Quercus palustris*)

As a shade and ornamental tree, the pin oak is unquestionably the most popular of all our native oaks. It has been extensively planted in home grounds, in city parks, and along streets and highways, since it grows quite rapidly and requires relatively little care. In youth it has a very symmetrical, pyramidlike crown of slender branches and glossy green leaves; the lowermost branches have a slight tendency to droop. Its trunk is straight, and continues from the base to the tip of the tree. The side branches are never very large, but have a great many short, stiff shoots or pinlike branchlets, from which the tree gets its common name. Old trees gradually develop broader and more open crowns.

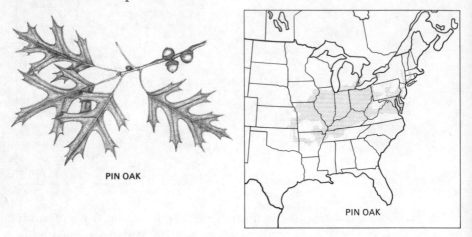

PIN OAK

PIN OAK

In summer the pin oak has leaves 3 to 5 inches in length, with deep indentations between the usually five bristle-tipped and bristle-toothed lobes. They are bright green and lustrous above, slightly paler and smooth or nearly so beneath. In autumn they turn red, but without the brilliance of the scarlet oak. The little, pale brown, often striped acorns are half an inch or less in diameter, and are seated in shallow saucerlike cups. They are just about the right size to make good meals for wood ducks, ruffed grouse, wild turkeys, and blue jays.

Unlike the scarlet oak, the pin oak is a tree of the bottomlands. It commonly grows along streams with such trees as the silver maple, American elm, sycamore, and sweetgum. The scientific name *palustris* means "of marshes." Trees 70 to 80 feet high, with trunks 2 to 3 feet in diameter, are about average; but occasionally one may be as much as 120 feet high, with a trunk diameter of up to about 5 feet. A champion growing at Saint Davids,

Pennsylvania, is 135 feet tall with a branch spread about the same, and its trunk is 16 feet in circumference at 4½ feet above the ground.

The natural range of the pin oak extends from Massachusetts west to southeastern Iowa, and southward into central North Carolina, Tennessee, and northeastern Oklahoma.

## BLACK OAK (*Quercus velutina*)

Not many oaks have leaves as variable as those of the black oak. Typically they are 3 to about 7 inches long, and like those of most other members of the red oak tribe, they have lobes which are both bristle-tipped and bristle-toothed. The indentations between the lobes vary in depth,

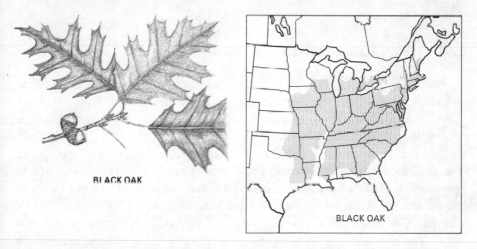

BLACK OAK

BLACK OAK

however, from rather shallow to very deep. They are tough and somewhat leathery in texture, lustrous dark green above, the lower surface a paler and duller yellowish-green and coated with a powdery down. In the fall they turn a dull red or brown. The scientific name *velutina,* meaning "velvety," refers to the downiness of the young leaves in spring.

Some other distinctive features of the black oak are its rather large, pointed buds, which are coated with a dull whitish down, and the bright orange or yellow color of its inner bark. On the trunks of larger trees the blackish outer bark is deeply furrowed and broken into block-like ridges. The acorns, too, are sufficiently distinctive to help in identifying the tree. They are from ½ to ¾ inch long, light reddish-brown, and about half enclosed by a deep top-shaped cup on which the upper rows of scales have loose and spreading tips. The kernels of these acorns are yellow and intensely bitter.

The black oak grows from southwestern Maine westward through southern Ontario to southeastern Minnesota, and southward to northern Florida and eastern Texas. It occurs most abundantly in the dry uplands, but grows best on rich and moist but well-drained soils. The usual height is only 50 or 60 feet, with a trunk 2 to 3 feet in diameter; trees in the open develop an irregular but wide-spreading crown. The champion registered by the American Forestry Association—a tree at Warrensville Heights, Ohio—is 125 feet in height, with a branch spread of 85 feet and a trunk circumference of 22 feet 3 inches at 4½ feet above ground.

The wood of the black oak is sold simply as "red oak lumber." Its tannin-rich bark has been used for tanning hides, and a yellow pigment called "quercitron," obtained from the inner bark, was formerly used in dyeing cloth.

## SOUTHERN RED OAK (*Quercus falcata*)

Among the members of the red oak tribe, the southern red oak—or Spanish oak, as it is often called—is readily distinguished by its leaves, which are lustrous dark green above and permanently coated on the lower surface with a yellowish-gray to whitish down.

One variety of this tree grows on the dry soils of the uplands, throughout the piedmont and well into the lower mountains. Its leaves have three to five sharply pointed, sparingly bristle-toothed lobes, and usually rounded bases, the end lobe being much longer than the others and often slightly curved. The name *falcata,* which means "sickle-shaped," refers to the end lobe. The lowland variety—which is often called the swamp red oak or cherrybark oak—has leaves that are whiter beneath, usually pointed at the base, and often quite shallowly lobed. Both varieties have a dark brownish-gray bark with narrow ridges and shallow furrows; and both bear roundish orange-brown acorns about half an inch in diameter, seated in shallow, saucerlike cups.

Both the upland and the lowland variety grow to be large trees, commonly 70 to 80 feet high with a trunk 2 to 3 feet in diameter; specimens over 100 feet in height and with much greater trunk diameters are not unusual. The American Forestry Association has recorded a champion of the upland variety growing at Cumberstone, Maryland, with a height of 122 feet, a branch spread of 132 feet, and a trunk 24 feet 1 inch in circumference at 4½ feet above ground. A tree of the lowland variety in Richland County, South Carolina, has a height of 132 feet, a branch spread of 112 feet, and a trunk circumference of 18 feet 6 inches.

The southern red oak grows from southeastern New York southward into central Florida, west to eastern Texas, and north in the Mississippi Valley to the southern portions of Indiana and Illinois. It is also found in an isolated area in the upper Ohio Valley, extending from Ohio into West Virginia. In the southeastern states this is one of the commonest and best-known oaks, and it is widely planted as a shade tree. It is to be seen in virtually every city and town, as well as throughout the rural areas of the southeast. Many such trees are centuries old and doubtless have some historical association. In the open the southern red oak is a handsome and enduring tree with a big, broad, round-topped crown.

SOUTHERN RED OAK

SOUTHERN RED OAK

Aside from purely local use, the upland variety has never been rated very highly as a timber tree. On the other hand, the swamp red oak is noted in the lower Mississippi Valley, where it grows most abundantly, for the superior quality of its lumber—which is marketed, of course, simply as "red oak lumber."

## WATER OAK (*Quercus nigra*)

The water oak is one of the commonest trees of the South Atlantic and Gulf Coast States, where it grows in low wet places and along streams. It is most abundant in the coastal plain, although it follows many of the water-courses inland to the foothills. In addition, it is one of the most popular of oaks as both a shade and a street tree. Along the Atlantic coast it grows from central Florida northward to New Jersey. In the Mississippi Valley its range extends north into southeastern Missouri and eastern Oklahoma, and it grows westward well into eastern Texas.

For variety of leaf form, no other native oak surpasses the water oak. Its short-stalked leaves measure from 2 to about 5 inches in length. Most often they are blunt or rounded at the broad tip, and taper to a pointed base. Quite frequently, however, they are three-lobed toward the tip, and they may have several side lobes. Especially on young trees, the leaves are often long and narrow, resembling those of the willow oak. In the warmer coastal regions the leaves often remain green until late winter, but inland they turn yellow and drop in the fall.

The little acorns—usually less than half an inch in diameter—are roundish, nearly black in color, and often striped. They are seated in shallow, saucerlike cups which have downy, close-fitting scales. The kernels are bright orange, and though they are very bitter, they are eaten by wood ducks, wild turkeys, blue jays, and many other birds and mammals.

Water oaks are usually 60 to 70 feet in height, with a trunk from 2 to 3 feet in diameter. An exceptionally large specimen may attain a height of as much as 125 feet and have a trunk between 4 and 6 feet in diameter. A current champion recorded by the American Forestry Association grows near Center, Texas. It has a height of 77 feet, a branch spread of 100 feet, and a trunk circumference of 20 feet 3 inches at 4½ feet above the ground.

The scientific name *nigra,* meaning "black," evidently refers to the dark color of the acorns and possibly also to the blackish bark.

## WILLOW OAK (*Quercus phellos*)

Some oaks have leaves that do not at all conform to the customary idea of what an oak leaf should look like, and one of these is the willow oak. Its narrowly lance-shaped, short-stalked, smooth-edged leaves are from 2 to 5

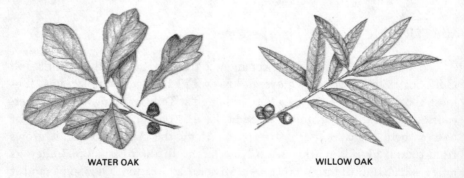

WATER OAK                                    WILLOW OAK

inches long. Usually quite smooth, and a light green that turns yellow in the fall, they look more like the leaves of a willow than of an oak.

The little, rounded acorns of the willow oak are light yellowish-brown or greenish-brown in color, and are seated in thin, shallow, saucerlike cups. Like the acorns of other members of the red oak tribe, they do not mature until the fall of the second year. Though bitter, they are eaten by many wild birds and mammals.

The willow oak grows in bottomlands and along streams from southeastern New York and New Jersey southward to Georgia and northwestern Florida, west to eastern Texas, and northward through the Mississippi Valley to southern Illinois and Missouri. In the Carolinas it ranges inland to the foothills of the mountains. Throughout most of its range it grows to a height of 60 to 80 feet and has a trunk 2 to 3 feet in diameter; but in the South, trees 80 to 100 or more feet in height, with trunks 3 to 5 feet in diameter, are not uncommon. The champion described by the American Forestry Association is a tree at Queenstown, on the eastern shore of Maryland. It has a height of 118 feet, a branch spread of 106 feet, and a trunk with a breast-high circumference of 21 feet 2 inches.

Open-grown willow oaks develop a beautiful, dense, symmetrical crown that is oval or round-topped in shape. As a shade or ornamental tree the species is widely planted throughout the South Atlantic and Gulf Coast States. In the lower Mississippi Valley it is a timber tree of considerable commercial importance, the wood being marketed as "red oak lumber."

The scientific name *phellos,* given by Linnaeus, was the ancient Greek name for the cork oak of southern Europe.

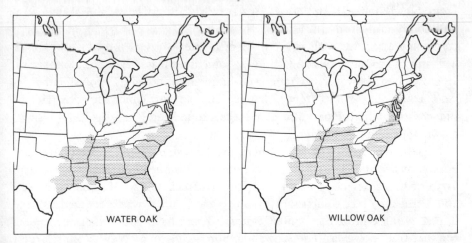

WATER OAK                    WILLOW OAK

# ELM FAMILY

## AMERICAN ELM (*Ulmus americana*)

❧ OF all our native trees none is better known or more universally admired than the American elm. It is a large tree—the largest of six native elms —and in the open its great trunk usually divides close to the ground into several large branches, forming a massive vase-shaped or wide-spreading, round-topped crown. The drooping branches give an air of grace and dignity that few other trees can match. The early colonists, quick to take advantage of its virtues, planted American elms on the commons and along the streets of towns all through New England, so that the section has long been famous for its fine big elms. When the tide of civilization moved westward, so did the custom of planting elms. This, the choicest of all American shade trees, has been made the state tree in Massachusetts, North Dakota, and Nebraska.

The American elm grows naturally in bottomlands and along streams from Newfoundland and Nova Scotia westward to eastern Saskatchewan, and south into northern Florida and eastern Texas. In swampy places it commonly associates with red and silver maples, swamp and pin oaks, black ash, and the cottonwoods and willows; sometimes it is called the swamp elm. It grows best, however, in rich, well-drained bottomlands. Forest elms develop columnlike trunks from 2 to 4 feet in diameter, which are often free of branches for 50 feet or more above the ground, and usually have a small crown with arching branches.

It is in the open that the American elm achieves its greatest size and beauty. When the Great Elm at Wethersfield, Connecticut, was measured in 1930, it had a height of about 100 feet, a branch spread of about 150 feet, and a trunk 29 feet 6 inches in circumference; and it was acclaimed as "the largest living elm in the United States." There have been other contenders for that title, however. The Gowanda Elm—said to be New York's largest tree—was reported as having a trunk 39 feet in circumference near the ground, without limbs to 50 feet from the ground, where its girth was 20 feet, and a height of 100 feet. A more recent champion, according to the American Forestry Association, is a tree near Trigonia in Blount County, Tennessee. It has a height of 160 feet, a branch spread of 147 feet, and a trunk measuring 24 feet 7 inches at 4½ feet above ground.

Many great old elms quite naturally have been associated with historic events and notable people. New England, of course, is full of such trees, but there are others farther to the west. Ohio had its famous Logan Elm, beneath which Lord Dunmore, the colonial governor of Virginia, made a treaty with Chief Cornstalk of the Shawnees and Chief Logan of the Mingos, two years before the American Revolution. Chief Logan declined to

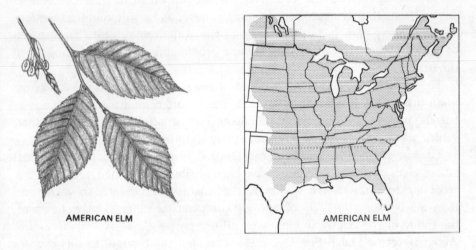

AMERICAN ELM

AMERICAN ELM

be present, but he sent a message which is still rated as a classic of Indian oratory. Kentucky had its famous elm at Boonesboro, under which, in May 1775, the backwoodsmen gathered to establish some form of local government and devise measures for the protection of settlers living west of the Alleghenies and south of the Ohio. Iowa has its Buffalo Bill Elm, in whose shade the famous frontiersman played as a boy; and Kansas has a pair of famous elms—one associated with General George A. Custer and the other with the noted frontiersman Kit Carson.

Other great elms have passed from the scene but not from memory. One such was the Washington Elm at Cambridge, Massachusetts, under which George Washington is said to have taken command of the American Revolutionary forces in 1775. Almost equally famous was the Penn Treaty Elm at Shackamaxon, Pennsylvania, now part of the Kensington section of Philadelphia. In its shade William Penn concluded his memorable treaty with the

Indians in 1682. Although both of these elms are gone, many descendants still grow in various parts of the country.

With the first warm weather of spring, often as early as February or early March, little clusters of flowers burst from the larger and plumper buds on the twigs of the elm. Later, in March or April, the branches show the first flush of green as the little one-seeded fruits mature; and the trees are often full of goldfinches and purple finches, musically twittering as they dine on the seeds. By the time the new leafy shoots emerge from their buds, most if not all of the fruits are gone.

In summer the trees are clad in dark-green leaves 4 to 6 inches long. They appear lopsided, because the two sides of the leaf are unequal, and are doubly toothed along the edges. Often the upper surface of the leaf is smooth; sometimes it is slightly rough, but never as harshly rough as the leaf of the slippery elm. In fall the leaves of the American elm turn from green to golden yellow, and often they become brown and dry before falling from the tree.

The wood of the elm is but moderately heavy and hard, and it has a cross-grain that makes it difficult to split. It is most often used for such things as barrels, baskets, boxes, and crates. Some elm wood is used for furniture, vehicle parts, and dairy, poultry, and apiary supplies.

The age attained by the American elm has been a subject of much speculation. Ages of 300 to 600 years have been attributed to some large trees; but according to foresters the species reaches maturity in about 150 years, and trees much over 175 years of age are comparatively rare. Today, however, the future of the American elm—and all our native elms—is very uncertain. About 1930 the Dutch Elm Disease was accidentally brought to this country in elm logs imported for the veneer industry. It has spread widely, and a great many treasured elms have been lost. The fungus that causes the disease is spread by elm bark beetles, which feed on living trees and breed in those that are dead or dying.

The disease begins as a wilting or yellowing of the leaves on one or several branches, and it spreads until the tree dies. To complicate matters, two other common elm diseases produce similar symptoms and positive identification can be made only by laboratory tests. If you suspect that a tree is infected cut off a branch and send a portion of it either to the Dutch Elm Disease Laboraory, Bureau of Entomology and Plant Quarantine, U.S. Department of Agriculture, Washington, D.C. 20025, or to your state agricultural college. Experts there can tell you whether your suspicions are correct, and if so you must be prepared to lose the tree. There is no known cure.

*Ulmus* is the classical Latin name for the elm.

## SLIPPERY ELM (*Ulmus rubra*)

To the uninitiated the name of the slippery elm may be something of an enigma. The thick ashy-gray to dark reddish-brown bark of its trunk is deeply furrowed, and breaks into large, loose plates. The ashy-colored or light grayish-brown twigs are rough to the touch. Even the upper surfaces of the large leaves feel like a coarse grade of sandpaper. There seems, in fact, nothing at all smooth or slippery about it. Yet any country boy who has ever chewed its twigs or inner bark, until he had a mouthful of slippery, slimy, though pleasant-tasting mucilage, knows just why it is called the slippery elm.

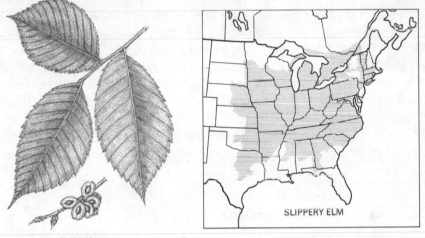

SLIPPERY ELM

SLIPPERY ELM

Compared with the American elm, there is nothing at all imposing about this tree. It lacks the grace and symmetry as well as the size of its better-known relative. Lumbermen cut it whenever they find one big enough to make a few boards, and they never distinguish its wood from that of the American elm. It goes to market as "elm lumber" and is used for the same purposes. Hardly anybody plants the slippery elm as a shade tree, nor is it ever used for reforestation purposes. The slippery elm has simply been left to shift for itself.

Ordinarily it is a tree of moderate size, sometimes 40 to 60 feet in height and with a trunk 1 or 2 feet in diameter. Occasionally on a favorable site, it attains a larger size, but a truly big slippery elm is rather rare. The American Forestry Association's champion is a tree growing near Henderson, Kentucky. It is 116 feet high, with a branch spread of 101 feet and a trunk measuring 21 feet 2 inches in circumference at 4½ feet above the ground.

Although the slippery elm prefers rich and moist but well-drained bottomlands, it often grows on the slopes and sometimes even on rocky ridges. Its range extends from Maine westward through southern Ontario and southwestward into eastern South Dakota, southward into northwestern Florida and eastern Texas. In many places it is rather rare, and there are very few areas where it could be called abundant. Usually it occurs here and there in forests dominated by other kinds of trees.

The mucilaginous inner bark of the tree has had many uses. It was eaten by the Indians and it does, indeed, contain a certain amount of nourishment. Pioneer woodsmen often chewed it to allay thirst. Steeped in water, it provided a medicine that was esteemed in frontier days, and is still used in rural households as a home remedy for the treatment of coughs, throat inflammations, and fever, and as a soothing poultice for sores and boils. In fact, despite the advent of supposedly better synthetic medicines, slippery elm bark has not entirely disappeared from pharmacy shelves or the official lists of drugs, and some old-fashioned country doctors still prescribe it, though its virtues are more often overlooked.

Red elm, another name often given to the slippery elm, and the scientific name *rubra,* also meaning "red," both refer to the rusty or reddish-brown buds that are conspicuous on the winter twigs.

## HACKBERRY (*Celtis occidentalis*)

In winter when a hackberry is naked, it may often be recognized by "witches' brooms"—dense, mistletoelike clusters of twigs—which a gall mite causes to grow on its branches. But even when the "brooms" are not present, the tree can usually be identified by its grayish-brown bark, which is roughened by characteristic corky warts and ridges. Moreover, it often has so ragged a look that one would never suppose it was a member of the elm family.

The hackberry is found more or less commonly from Massachusetts and New Hampshire westward through southern Ontario to central North Dakota, and southward to Georgia, Alabama, Arkansas, Kansas, and northeastern Colorado. In most places it is a rather small tree, 30 to 50 feet in height with a trunk from 1 to 2 feet in diameter. It grows best in bottomlands along the Ohio and Mississippi rivers, where it sometimes attains a height of up to 130 feet, with a trunk as much as 4 feet in diameter. The American Forestry Association records a champion near Wayland, Allegan County, Michigan, which is 113 feet tall, with a branch spread of 79 feet and a trunk measuring 18 feet in circumference at 4½ feet above ground. Another, at Granville, Ohio, is 75 feet high and has a trunk circumference of 16 feet 8 inches.

The leaves of the hackberry are placed alternately in two rows along slender, zig-zag branchlets. They are from 2 to 4½ inches long, egg-shaped or broadly lance-shaped and lop-sided or slanted at the base, and have three main veins arising from the summit of the short leaf stalk. Bright green and sometimes slightly rough on the upper surface, they are paler below, with edges sharply toothed except along the lower part.

Little, greenish, inconspicuous flowers appear on the branchlets along with the young leaves in April or May. The stamen bearing flowers grow in small clusters at the bases of the new leafy shoots, and those bearing pistils are in the axils of the new leaves. By September or October the latter have developed into pea-sized, brownish to dark purple, one-seeded fruits which have a thin but sugary flesh, with a flavor suggesting that of dates. Many kinds of birds are fond of hackberries, and so were the Indians; any that are not eaten may linger on the trees throughout the winter.

The wood is yellow or greenish-yellow in color, moderately heavy and hard, and fairly strong. Although the hackberry is not of any great commercial importance as a timber tree, its wood is sometimes used for furniture and boxes and crates. The hackberry is sometimes planted as a shade or ornamental tree, or for shelterbelts, particularly between the Mississippi River and the Rocky Mountains.

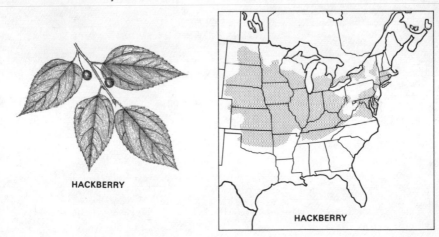

HACKBERRY

HACKBERRY

*Celtis,* a classical Latin name for a species of lotus, was applied by Linnaeus to the hackberries; and *occidentalis,* "western," refers to the Western Hemisphere.

Two other tree-sized hackberries are found in America. The sugarberry (*Celtis laevigata*) grows from Virginia south to Florida, west to Texas, and northward along the Mississippi Valley to southern Indiana, Missouri, and Oklahoma. It is distinguished by having smooth-edged or sparingly toothed and somewhat narrower leaves. The netleaf hackberry (*Celtis reticulata*), which also has smooth-edged leaves, grows in the West from Wyoming to western Washington, and southward to western Texas, northern Mexico, and southern California.

# MULBERRY FAMILY

## FLORIDA STRANGLER FIG (*Ficus aurea*)

❧ UNIQUE among North American trees is the Florida strangler fig, which grows in the coastal hammocks from Martin and Manatee counties southward to Everglades National Park and the Florida Keys. In many respects it resembles its famous cousin the banyan-tree (*Ficus bengalensis*) of India.

Although a seedling of the strangler fig is capable of living a terrestrial life from the start, more often it begins to grow as an epiphyte on the bark of some other tree, very often the cabbage palmetto. The roots grow downward around the trunk on which it is lodged, forming a trunk of its own about that of the host; and the dense crown it produces overhead meanwhile gradually shades out the crown of the ill-fated tree. By the time the strangler fig's own roots become established in the soil, the tree on which it started to grow is nearly or entirely dead, and the fig is a self-supporting tree. Eventually the larger branches produce aerial roots, which form new trunks whenever they reach the ground, just as they do in the banyan tree.

When mature the Florida strangler fig is a tree 40 to 50 feet in height, with a short trunk up to 3 feet in diameter and a broad, round-topped crown. The champion listed by the American Forestry Association—a tree in Miami's Bay Front Park—is 51 feet tall and has a trunk 22 feet 1 inch in circumference at 4½ feet above ground. Its simple evergreen leaves are leathery, dark green and shiny above, paler below, and from 1 to 4 inches long. They are elliptic in shape, smooth-edged, and more or less pointed at both ends; and a drop of milky sap will appear if one is broken from its branchlet.

The flowers of this fig are like those of all other figs—tiny, simple structures produced on the inside wall of a small, globe-shaped, fleshy receptacle.

139

As the branches lengthen, these receptacles are produced continuously in the axils of the leaves. After the flowers are pollinated, they become stalkless red receptacles about ¾ inch long, with little seedlike true fruits lining the inside. The edible part of any fig is such a receptacle, the "seeds" inside being the actual fruits.

The strangler fig is a handsome tree and is sometimes planted in Florida for ornamental purposes, but it has no other uses. The wood is exceedingly light, weak, and coarse-grained, and it lasts but a short time in contact with the ground. The "fruits," if you can call them that, are probably eaten by many birds, which appear to be the chief agency by which its seeds are dispersed.

*Ficus* is the classical Latin name of the fig, and *aurea* means "golden."

**FLORIDA STRANGLER FIG**

**FLORIDA STRANGLER FIG**

# MAGNOLIA FAMILY

## TULIP TREE (*Liriodendron tulipifera*)

❧ IN the Upper Cretaceous period—some 70 to 100 million years ago—several species of tulip trees grew in forests throughout the Northern Hemisphere. They have left fossil impressions of their leaves in the rocks of many lands; but during the Ice Age all but two of them vanished from the earth. One is the familiar tulip tree of our eastern forests. The other is a similar tree which grows in the central part of China.

The tulip tree is one of the largest, most distinctive, and most valuable of American broad-leaved trees. Its leaves, which cannot be confused with those of any other tree, have a shape strongly suggestive of a keystone. Commonly from 4 to 6 inches broad, they are rather rectanglar in outline, usually four-lobed, with a V-shaped notch at the broad summit. The upper surfaces are a dark, glossy green and the undersides are paler and slightly whitened. The slender leaf stalks are often almost as long as the blades. In autumn the leaves turn a beautiful golden yellow.

In May or June, cup-shaped, greenish-yellow flowers with orange centers appear at the tips of the branchlets. These flowers—which somewhat resemble the bloom of a tulip—have given the tree both its common and scientific names. *Liriodendron* combines two Greek words meaning "lily" and "tree"; and *tulipifera* means "bearing tulips." The nectar-laden flowers attract hordes of bees, and beekeepers thus regard the tulip tree as an important source of honey. Clustered in the center of each flower is a cone composed of many pistils, which develop into a cone-shaped cluster of dry fruits, each with a terminal wing and a four-angled base containing a seed. Squirrels and some birds often eat the seeds in the late fall and winter months, but enough are always left to assure new generations of tulip trees.

During the winter it is easy to recognize the tulip tree by its spicy-aromatic twigs with big flattened buds at their tips. The buds resemble miniature ducks' bills or beaver tails.

The tulip tree is found from southern New England west to Wisconsin, and southward into northern Florida and nearly to the Gulf coast, but it attains its best development in the southern Appalachians and in the lower Ohio Valley. Trees in virgin forests commonly attained a height of 100 to 150 feet and had trunks from 4 to 8 feet in diameter. Some were even said to be 200 feet tall and to have had trunk diameters of as much as 12 feet. A current champion recorded by the American Forestry Association—a tree at Amelia, Virginia—has a height of 110 feet, a branch spread of 119 feet, and a trunk 24 feet 3 inches in circumference at 4½ feet above the ground. The largest sound tulip tree in the Great Smoky Mountains National Park measures 23 feet 7 inches in circumference, but the park has many other majestic specimens. In the open a young tree has a characteristic cone-shaped crown, but with age the crown spreads and becomes more open. Forest tulip trees have tall, straight trunks which are without branches for a great distance above the ground.

Although botanists and horticulturists—and most nature-lovers—prefer the name of tulip tree, foresters and lumbermen invariably call this tree either the yellow poplar or, sometimes, the tulip poplar. But a poplar it is

**TULIP TREE**

not. Rather, it is a member of the magnolia family, and nowise related to the true poplars. All the same, though in some parts of the country it is called the whitewood, no lumberman would think of calling the tulip tree's soft, straight grained, easily worked, light yellowish-brown wood anything but "yellow poplar" or simply "poplar." The best of it today goes into such things as furniture, interior finish, siding, woodenware, and musical instruments. Lower-grade wood is used as core stock for plywood, slack cooperage staves, boxes and crates, excelsior, and pulpwood.

On the campus of St. John's College at Annapolis, Maryland, is a giant tulip tree under which the colonists and Indians made a treaty of peace in 1652. At the beginning of the American Revolution, the patriots of Annapolis assembled beneath its branches, and there also the people gathered to celebrate peace when the war ended. Thus it is often called the Liberty Tree or the Treaty Tree. Another ancient tree associated with early days is the Hendrick Hudson Tulip Tree, which stands in Inwood Park on the northern end of Manhattan Island, in New York City. It is said to be the only living thing on the island that was also there during Hudson's time.

The tulip tree is one of the finest and handsomest of trees for planting in parks, on home grounds, and along the wider streets. In youth, at least, it grows quite rapidly, but it does not reach maturity until it is about 200 years of age. Three states—Indiana, Kentucky, and Tennessee—have all selected this as their state tree.

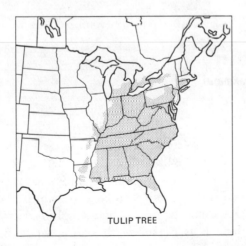

TULIP TREE

## SOUTHERN MAGNOLIA (*Magnolia grandiflora*)

Before the days of settlement, the southern magnolia grew wild along the streams and in the swamps of the South Atlantic and Gulf coastal plains from North Carolina south into central Florida and west to eastern Texas. Now it is often seen as an ornamental tree throughout much of the Southeast, inland as far as the foothills of the mountains. It has proved hardy as far north as Washington, D.C., where a magnificent specimen grows near the south portico of the White House, planted by President Andrew Jackson in memory of his wife Rachel.

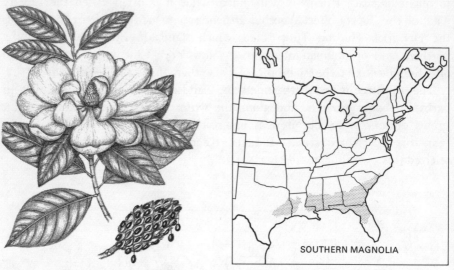

SOUTHERN MAGNOLIA

SOUTHERN MAGNOLIA

This magnolia is a splendid evergreen tree, with a cylindrical or pyramidal crown, and with elliptical, leathery, dark-green leaves so glossy above that each one seems to have been individually polished. On the underside they are usually coated with a wool which eventually becomes rusty-brown. The tree would be ornamental simply for its beautiful foliage, but in May and June it is decked with creamy-white flowers, usually 8 inches across. (The scientific name *grandiflora* means "large-flowered.") Each lemon-scented blossom has from six to a dozen petals and three sepals of the same whiteness.

As a rule the tree grows to a height of 60 to 80 feet and has a trunk from 2 to 3 feet in diameter. A champion, according to the American Forestry Association, is a tree growing at Baton Rouge, Louisiana. It has a height of 99 feet, a branch spread of 71 feet, and a trunk measuring 18 feet in circumference at 4½ feet above the ground. Southern magnolias usually attain their greatest proportions in the lower Mississippi Valley, but Coker and Totten in *Trees of the Southeastern States* mention one at Como in Hertford County, North Carolina, the trunk of which measured 5 feet 2½ inches in diameter at 4½ feet above ground, and whose branches had a spread of 82 feet. This tree is known as the Old Waddell Magnolia.

The magnolia has a yellowish-white wood that becomes brown upon exposure. It is moderately heavy and hard, usually has a straight grain, and shrinks very little. Mostly it is used for furniture and venetian blinds. Some magnolia wood goes into sashes, doors, boxes, and veneer. Louisiana leads in the production of magnolia lumber today, and Mississippi is probably a close second. Mississippi—the "Magnolia State"—has made the southern magnolia its state tree. Louisiana has chosen the magnolia as its state flower.

Geologists tell us that magnolias have been on the earth for as much as 80 to 100 million years. The ancestors of our present-day species were growing in the forests while the great dinosaurs still roamed the earth. Botanists remind us that the magnolia is a very primitive type of flower, in that all of the floral parts are spirally arranged, like the scales of a pine cone. In the center of the magnolia blossom, numerous pistils spiral about a cone-shaped receptacle, and below them a great many stamens are similarly arranged. The pistils develop into a tight cluster of fruits, and at maturity each individual fruit splits open along one side, releasing one or two fleshy, scarlet-coated seeds, which dangle for awhile on slender threads.

The genus *Magnolia* was named by Linnaeus in honor of Pierre Magnol, physician to King Louis XIV of France and director of a botanical garden at Montpellier. For ages the Chinese have cultivated magnolias, and in China the buds have been used both medicinally and for seasoning rice. Horticulturists still treasure the magnolias as being among the most beautiful of all flowering trees.

## CUCUMBER TREE (*Magnolia acuminata*)

A total of some thirty-five species of magnolia are found in the Himalayas, China, Japan, southern Mexico, and the eastern United States. Seven or eight of these are native to our southeastern states, but only the hardy cucumber tree ventures far enough north actually, though just barely, to cross the Canadian border. It is found from central Georgia westward to southeastern Oklahoma, and northward to western New York, extreme southern Ontario, and the southern portions of Indiana and Illinois. Nowhere is it more abundant, however, than in the southern Appalachian region, where it sometimes occurs at elevations of 5,000 feet. It thrives in the cooler uplands, shunning the warm and humid coastal plain which is the domain of the sweetbay (*Magnolia virginiana*) and the southern magnolia.

In most places this leaf-losing magnolia is a tree of quite ordinary dimensions—50 to 80 feet in height, with a trunk from 1 to rarely 3 feet in diameter. But in the fertile coves and valleys at the base of the mountains in Kentucky, Tennessee, and the Carolinas, cucumber trees are often 100 feet or more tall, with trunks 4 to 5 feet or more in diameter. Often the great trunks of these forest trees are clear of branches for 50 or more feet above ground. Perhaps the largest cucumber tree ever recorded stood in the Greenbrier section of Great Smoky Mountains National Park. It was 125 feet in height, and its trunk, at 4½ feet above the ground, was 18 feet 4 inches in circumference.

In summer a cucumber tree may be known by its alternate, oval or egg-shaped, smooth-edged, thin leaves, which are pointed to rounded at the base and pointed at the tip—hence the scientific name *acuminata,* meaning "pointed," refers to the leaves. They are 5 to 10 inches long, dark yellowish-green above, paler and sometimes softly hairy beneath. The twigs, like those of all magnolias, have a line encircling them at each point where a leaf is attached; and if bruised or broken, they give off a pleasant spicy odor. Borne on the twigs are greenish-gray buds with a coat of silvery, silky hairs.

At some time between April and June the trees come into blossom, but their flowers have no odor and are rather inconspicuous compared with those of other magnolias. Bell-shaped and from 2½ to 3½ inches long, they stand erect at the tips of the branchlets. Usually they are greenish-yellow, but those of a variety called the yellow cucumber tree, which is found rather rarely in the southern Appalachian region, are a bright canary yellow.

The tree gets its common name from a fancied resemblance of the compact fruit cluster while it is still green, to a cucumber. Later in summer the fruit clusters become pinkish and finally purplish-red. Then each fruit in the cluster splits down the outside, and the seeds with their bright scarlet, fleshy coats emerge, to dangle for awhile on slender threads before they drop to the ground.

The forest-grown cucumber tree produces a wood so similar to that of its distant cousin the tulip tree that lumbermen do not usually trouble to make any distinction between the two. It all goes on the market as "yellow poplar" lumber. In the open the cucumber tree develops a short trunk and a symmetrical, broadly cone-shaped crown, and it is often planted as a shade or ornamental tree.

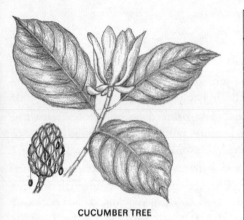

CUCUMBER TREE

CUCUMBER TREE

# LAUREL FAMILY

## SASSAFRAS (*Sassafras albidum*)

❧ IN the years following the first settlements along the Atlantic coast of the United States, the sassafras had a brief heyday of fame. Apparently it all started about the year 1574, when Nicholas Monardes published a glowing account of the marvelous virtues and healing powers of the wood and root of a New World tree called the sassafras. Soon the sassafras was famous throughout Europe for its supposed medicinal virtues, and became the object of many an intensive search; in 1602 the price on the English market had risen to the fabulous sum of 336 pounds sterling per ton. The wood and bark of the tree were among the first exports sent to England by Captain John Smith from the Jamestown Colony of Virginia, and for some years the highly prized tree brought many a fortune-hunting party to America. But in the end the sassafras failed to live up to its vaunted reputation, people lost faith in it, and as a source of great fortunes it proved a dismal disappointment.

The sassafras still grows in woodlands and along roadsides and fencerows all the way from southern New England west to Wisconsin and Iowa, and southward into northern Florida and the Gulf coast. Although often it is little more than a shrub, it sometimes becomes a fair-sized tree. According to the American Forestry Association, one near Owensburg, Kentucky, is 88½ feet tall and has a trunk 16 feet in circumference at 4½ feet above ground; and another near Mt. Nebo in Lancaster County, Pennsylvania, has a height of 65 feet with a trunk circumference of 15 feet 4 inches.

The sassafras is a member of the laurel family, and as such it is a distant cousin of the famous laurel (*Laurus nobilis*), with which prize-winning athletes in ancient Greece and Rome were crowned—a custom still referred to in speaking of a person who has "earned his laurels." Like those of other members of this family, the various parts of the sassafras—roots, stems, leaves, flowers, and fruits—are decidedly aromatic. The bark of its roots, gathered in the early spring, has been used since early colonial days for brewing the pleasant-tasting "sassafras tea"; and occasionally one still finds little bundles of the root bark offered for sale in market places. Oil of sassafras, distilled from the roots, is used to flavor medicines, candies, and sometimes the glue on stamps. In parts of the South the mucilaginous young leaves, and the pith of the branchlets, are dried, powdered, and used to thicken soups. By no stretch of the imagination can the sassafras be called a valuable timber tree, but since its wood is durable in contact with the soil, farmers often use the trunks as fence posts.

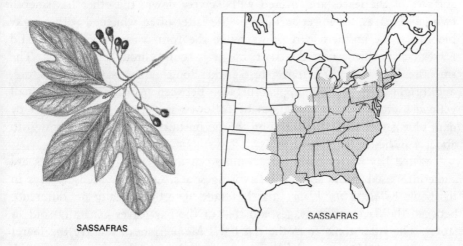

SASSAFRAS

SASSAFRAS

In early spring, before its leaves appear, the sassafras puts forth rather showy little clusters of honey-yellow flowers which attract the bees. All summer long the tree may be known by its aromatic leaves, most of which are oval-shaped, though often on the same branch there will be some shaped like mittens and others that have three lobes. In fall the leaves turn yellow or orange, often tinged with red; and thus the sassafras adds its bit to the color of an Eastern autumn. In the fall, too, its berrylike but one-seeded dark-blue fruits are borne on club-shaped stalks of a most vivid red.

*Sassafras* is a Spanish name, perhaps of American Indian origin, and *albidum* means "whitish."

## RED BAY (*Persea borbonia*)

The evergreen red bay, or swampbay, grows in the swamps of the coastal plain from southern Delaware and eastern Virginia south to the southern part of Florida, and west to southeastern and southern Texas. At times it may attain a height of 60 to 70 feet, with a trunk 2½ to 3 feet in diameter, but usually it is very much smaller. The American Forestry Association's champion is a tree near Conroe, Texas. It has a height of 53 feet, a branch spread of 50 feet, and its trunk measures 8 feet 6 inches in circumference at 4½ feet above the ground. The spicy odor given off when the leaves are bruised or the twigs are broken is quite similar to that of the sassafras, and serves very well to distinguish it.

The red bay occurs in two intergrading forms, which were formerly thought to be different species. In one of these, the twigs and the lower surfaces of the leaves are covered with velvety down; the other has smooth twigs and leaves, the lower surfaces of the latter often whitened with a waxy bloom. In the northern part of its range the form with smooth twigs and leaves occurs chiefly near the coast, but it is found throughout Florida. The smooth-edged leaves are from 3 to 6 inches long, rather leathery in texture, and bright-green on the upper surface. Between April and June, small yellowish-green flowers appear, to be followed in September or October by dark-blue fruits about ½ inch long, borne on upright red stalks from ½ to about 2 inches in length.

The red bay has practically no commercial importance, but its leaves are sometimes used in the South for flavoring soups. Oliver P. Medsger says in his book *Edible Wild Plants* that he could detect practically no difference between the flavor of its leaves and that of the bay leaves generally sold in stores. The latter come from the red bay's Mediterranean relative the laurel or sweet bay (*Laurus nobilis*). Another and even closer relative is the avocado (*Persea americana*), a native of the American tropics often cultivated in Florida for its fruits.

*Persea* is an ancient Greek name for an unknown Egyptian tree, with fruit growing directly on the stem, and *borbonia* is a name which some earlier botanists used for this genus of plants.

## CALIFORNIA LAUREL (*Umbellularia californica*)

The California laurel, or Oregon myrtle, is the only member of the laurel family found in western North America, and it is also the largest North American member of the family. On the most favorable bottomland sites in southwestern Oregon and in California's "Redwood Empire," it becomes a tree 100 to 175 feet in height, with a trunk from 3 to 6 feet or more in diameter. Elsewhere it is usually a smaller tree, 40 to 80 feet tall with a trunk diameter of 1½ to 2½ feet; and on thin, dry, rocky soils it may be merely a large shrub. Along the wind-swept bluffs of the Pacific it occurs as a prostrate shrub with spreading, thickly matted branches. A champion re-

corded by the American Forestry Association—a tree near Eleanor in
Humboldt County, California—has a trunk 36 feet 9 inches in circumference at 4½ feet above the ground.

California laurel may be distinguished at once from other trees in its
range by the strong, camphorlike, pungent odor given off by its leaves and
its yellowish-green branchlets when they are crushed. The evergreen leaves
are elliptic or lance-shaped, leathery, dark-green and shiny above, paler and
dull below. They range from 2 to about 5 inches in length, have smooth
edges, and are pointed at both ends. Between January and March, before
the new leaves appear, little clusters of yellowish-green flowers are produced
in the axils of the leaves of the previous year. Later come yellowish-green or

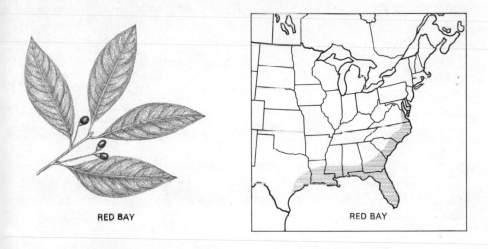

RED BAY                              RED BAY

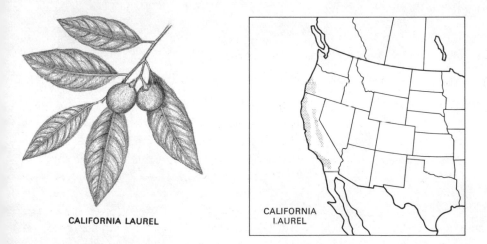

CALIFORNIA LAUREL          CALIFORNIA
                           LAUREL

purplish fruits which resemble olives. About an inch across, they have a single, large, thin-shelled seed, covered with a thin, leathery flesh.

The wood of the tree is highly prized by cabinet-makers, for no other excels the beauty of its grain after it has been finished. Very heavy when green, it becomes moderately heavy when dry. It is hard, very firm, fine-grained, a rich yellowish-brown in color, and often beautifully mottled. Cut into veneer, it is used for furniture and paneling. As lumber it is used for cabinet work, interior trim, and the manufacture of woodenware and novelties.

*Umbellularia* comes from the Latin word *umbellula,* "a small umbrella," and refers to the flower clusters or umbels.

# WITCH HAZEL FAMILY

## SWEET GUM (*Liquidambar styraciflua*)

❧ STAR-SHAPED leaves which give off a pleasant balsamic fragrance when bruised are a distinctive feature of the sweet gum. Another is the ball-shaped, burlike heads of fruits which dangle on long and slender stalks all through the fall and winter months. Still another is the corky ridges or winglike outgrowths which appear on the branchlets after the first year. No other tree in our forests has such a combination of features. As a result, the sweet gum is unmistakable.

One of the commonest trees in the southeastern United States, except in the higher mountains—above 2,000 to 2,500 feet—the sweet gum grows along the Atlantic coast from Connecticut south to central Florida, and from the Ohio Valley, southeastern Missouri, and eastern Oklahoma south

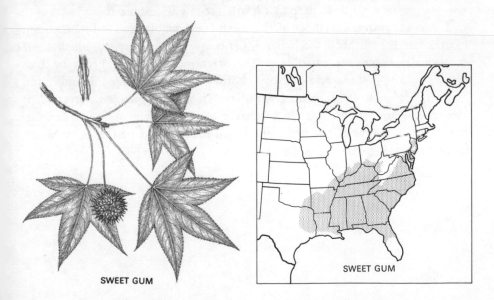

SWEET GUM

SWEET GUM

to the Gulf coast and Texas. Typically it is a bottomland tree. It is most abundant along streams, often in places which are occasionally flooded, but it cannot survive in swamps where water stands permanently. Quite often it is common on higher ground where the soil is at least reasonably moist.

The sweet gum at its best is a large tree, often 80 to 120 feet tall, and with a trunk from 3 to 4 feet in diameter. Really large specimens may attain heights up to 150 feet, and their trunks may have a diameter of as much as 5 feet. One growing at New Madrid, Missouri, the current champion listed by the American Forestry Association, has a height of 118 feet, a branch spread of 81 feet, and a trunk with a circumference of 17 feet 10 inches at 4½ feet above the ground. Young trees growing in the open have symmetrical, pyramidal crowns. At maturity the side branches become heavier, and the tree develops a rather egg-shaped but more or less irregular crown.

Not only is the sweet gum a fine tree for ornamental planting, but it is also one of the most important commercial hardwoods. Its wood is moderately heavy, hard, and strong, with an interlocking grain. Lumbermen divide the wood into two classes: sap gum, from the light-colored outer sapwood of the tree, and red gum, from the reddish-brown heartwood. As lumber it goes into furniture, into radio, television, and phonograph cabinets, and into interior trim, millwork, woodenware, and barrels. As veneer and plywood it is used for interior woodwork, baskets, boxes, and crates. The sweet gum is one of the finest of our native broad-leaved trees for ornamental planting, and is widely used as a shade and street tree. All summer long its star-shaped leaves are a lustrous dark green. In fall they turn bright red, orange, or a purple so deep that it often seems almost black.

The sweet gum is a member of the witch hazel family, and a distant cousin of the familiar shrubby witch hazel (*Hamamelis virginiana*), which itself occasionally becomes a small tree. The scientific name was given by Linnaeus in 1753. *Liquidambar,* two Latin words meaning "liquid" and "amber," refers to the fragrant resin of the tree, and *styraciflua,* "styrax-" or "storax-flowing," refers to a close relative of the sweet gum found in western Asia, the source of the storax used in medicines and perfumes, to which the gum exuded by the sweet gum is very similar.

# PLANETREE FAMILY

## AMERICAN SYCAMORE (*Platanus occidentalis*)

❧ ALONG streams and in bottomlands, from Maine to eastern Nebraska and south to northern Florida and central Texas, the American sycamore is one of the commonest trees. Often it is a big tree; for although not the tallest, it is certainly the most massive of all American hardwoods or broad-leaved trees. Even at a distance a sycamore may be recognized by the glistening whiteness of its branches and by its strikingly mottled trunk. The outer bark of the latter peels off in large flakes, leaving a patchwork of light brown, whitish, and greenish-gray.

Although we call this New World tree a sycamore, the true sycamore tree of the Bible, and the one that rightfully bears the name, is a species of fig. Our sycamore is a member of the planetree family, and *Platanus* is its classical Latin name. Sometimes it is called the buttonwood or buttonball tree, on account of its fruits, which are borne in closely-packed, ball-like heads which dangle on long, slender stalks. During the winter the heads break up and the little one-seeded dry fruits drift away, borne on parachutes of hairs. The leaves are maplelike, 4 to 8 inches broad, shallowly three- to five-lobed, and coarsely toothed; and the leaf stalks have hollow bases covering the one-scaled, cone-shaped buds.

The American sycamore often attains a height of 100 feet or more, with a trunk from 3 to 8 feet in diameter. Some have been known to reach a height of 175 feet and to have a trunk as much as 14 feet across, but big sycamores are more notable for the immense spread of their branches than for great height. The American Forestry Association's champion, growing near South Bloomfield, Ohio, has a trunk measuring 32 feet 10 inches in circumference 4½ feet above the ground. It is 80 feet high and has a spread of 102 feet. Pennsylvania's most massive tree is a sycamore growing four miles west of Lancaster. Little more than 100 feet high, its branches have a spread of 138 feet, and its trunk measures 22 feet in circumference at 5 feet above the ground.

Since American sycamores are said to live to an age of 500 or 600 years, it is only natural that many old sycamores have some connection with past historical events. Danbury, Connecticut, has its Revolutionary Sycamore, a tree that was standing at the time the town was settled in 1685, and that was on the line of the British soldiers' retreat to Ridgefield after they burned Danbury during the Revolutionary War. Pennsylvania has its historic Fort Hunter Buttonwood, associated with pioneer days, as were the Charlemont and Deerfield Buttonwoods in Massachusetts. The trunk of a big old sycamore is often hollow. Hollow sycamores frequently serve as den trees for

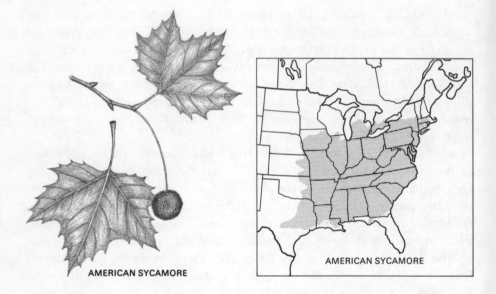

AMERICAN SYCAMORE

AMERICAN SYCAMORE

raccoons, or as the abode of barn owls. And about the year 1764, two brothers, Sam and John Pringle, who penetrated the unbroken wilderness of what is now West Virginia, lived for three years in the hollow trunk of a great sycamore tree. That tree has long since been gone, but another has taken its place and is still known as the Old Pringle Sycamore. It has a cavity in which three persons could easily take shelter.

The wood of the American sycamore is reddish-brown in color, moderately heavy and hard, and has an interlocking grain which makes it difficult either to work or to split. One of its principal uses is for butchers' blocks. It is also used for flooring, furniture, handles, slack cooperage, boxes and crates, and in the form of veneer for making baskets and berry boxes.

The growth of the American sycamore is rather rapid, at least during its earlier years, and it is often planted as a shade or ornamental tree. More often planted along city streets, however, is the so-called London planetree, believed to be a hybrid between the American sycamore and the Oriental planetree. Usually it has two ball-like heads of fruits on each dangling stalk, whereas the American sycamore generally has but one.

Two other species belonging to this genus occur in the western United States. One is the Arizona sycamore (*Platanus wrightii*), found along stream banks and on canyon walls in southern Arizona and southwestern New Mexico. Its leaves have from five to seven deep lobes, and from two to four ball-like fruit heads are borne along each string. The other species is the California sycamore (*Platamus racemosa*), whose leaves have three to five deep and narrow lobes; from two to seven ball-like fruit heads develop on each dangling stalk. Neither is an important timber tree although the California sycamore attains a large size. One near Santa Barbara listed in the American Forestry Association's roster of big trees is 116 feet high with a branch spread of 158 feet, and its trunk at 4½ feet from the ground is 27 feet in circumference.

# ROSE FAMILY

## BLACK CHERRY (*Prunus serotina*)

❦ THE black cherry—the largest North American tree belonging to the rose family—has a wide range, from Nova Scotia westward to southeastern Manitoba, and southward to northern Florida and eastern Texas. Throughout this range it is found commonly in forests and woodlots, along fencerows, and by the roadside.

Usually it is no more than a medium-sized tree, 50 to 60 feet in height and with a trunk from 2 to 3 feet in diameter. In the virgin forests, however, it often attained a height of 100 feet or more, and the trunk—sometimes as much as 5 feet in diameter—would be straight and clear of branches for 50 feet or more above the ground. Such big wild cherries were choice timber trees, but are seldom seen today. Some of them survive in the Tionesta Tract of the Allegheny National Forest in Pennsylvania, and in the forests of Great Smoky Mountains National Park. The current champion listed by the American Forestry Association—a tree growing at Lawrence in Van Buren County, Michigan—has a height of 102 feet, a branch spread of 89 feet, and a trunk 23 feet 4 inches in circumference at 4½ feet above the ground.

In the open the black cherry has a relatively short trunk, which divides into several large branches to form a more or less spreading, oval-shaped, and fairly open crown. It is readily distinguished by its reddish-brown twigs, which are more or less covered with a gray skin, and have a distinctive bitter-almond odor when broken. The lustrous, dark-green, oblong-shaped leaves also give off this odor when they are bruised. In late spring or early summer one can often spot a black cherry by the glistening white webs of tent caterpillars, which find the foliage much to their liking, and are sometimes so numerous that they completely defoliate the tree.

During April or May, while the new leaves still have a reddish hue, showy clusters of little white flowers appear at the tips of the branchlets. By late summer they have developed into drooping clusters of pea-sized cherries, which first turn a dark red but finally become a purple so dark that it seems almost black. The better fruits have a juicy pulp with a winy, bittersweet taste that is pleasing to many palates. As soon as the fruits ripen, the trees swarm with robins, catbirds, cedar waxwings, and many other birds, and before long all of the ripe cherries have been stripped from the branches. This is just what nature intends, for the seeds, protected by their bony covering, pass unharmed through a bird's digestive tract and are thus scattered widely over the countryside, where many have a chance to grow into young trees. The seeds themselves, however, are relished by chipmunks, flying squirrels, and white-footed mice.

The heartwood of the black cherry varies in color from light to dark reddish-brown. It is moderately heavy, hard, and strong, and has a distinctive luster. The color of the wood, like that of mahogany, deepens with age, and next to the black walnut it is rated the finest cabinet wood produced by a North American tree. It is the wood used exclusively for mounting electrotype plates and zinc etchings for printing, and it is always in demand for furniture, gunstocks, and interior paneling. When railroad coaches and streetcars were still made of wood, a great many of them had cherry paneling, which today would be prohibitively expensive.

The inner bark of the tree is a time-honored ingredient of cough medicines, and although still listed as an official remedy, it is no longer in great demand. The bitter-almond odor of the bark, as well as the leaves, is due to the presence of hydrocyanic, or prussic, acid. Cattle and sheep usually will not eat the leaves when more palatable forage is abundant; but if they do, the results more often than not prove fatal.

*Prunus* comes from the classical Latin word for "plum," and *serotina,* meaning "late," refers to the relatively late maturing of the fruit.

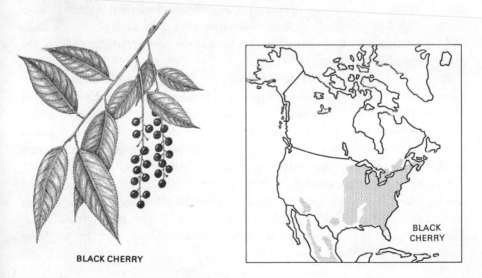

BLACK CHERRY

BLACK CHERRY

# PULSE FAMILY

### EASTERN REDBUD (*Cercis canadensis*)

❧ IN early spring, blushing eastern redbuds show up on rocky hillsides, along streams, in mountain coves, and along the borders of woodlands. They are part of the spring display from Connecticut and southern New York westward through southern Ontario to eastern Nebraska, south into northern Florida, eastern Texas, and Mexico. In Oklahoma, where the redbud has been made the state tree, it transforms thousands of ravines and creek bottoms into winding ribbons of magenta-pink. Wherever it grows, the blossoming redbud is one of the glories of spring.

The first published record of the tree came not from our own country but from our neighbor to the south, in the year 1570, when Philip II, King of Spain, sent his physician, Dr. Francisco Hernandez, to investigate the "natural history, antiquities, and political conditions" of Mexco. The learned doctor gave to the world the first published description of the showy-flowered little tree, which was introduced into cultivation as early as 1641. Both George Washington and Thomas Jefferson were admirers of the redbud, and Washington's diary mentions specimens he had transplanted to the grounds of Mount Vernon.

In the warmer parts of the lower South, the clusters of little, pealike, rosy-pink blossoms often cover the boughs of the trees as early as February; but in most places it is often late March or April before they appear. Everywhere they will have passed their peak before the tiny new leaves begin to unfold. It is said that the flower buds, blossoms, and young pods make very good fritters; in Mexico the fried flowers are considered a delicacy.

During the summer the redbud is easy to recognize by its heart-shaped leaves, which are 3 to 5 inches broad, with smooth edges and veins that radiate from the summit of the leaf stalk like the fingers of a spread hand. The thin, flattened, pealike pods average about 3 inches in length, and remain on the branches for a long time. Each one contains about half a dozen brown seeds, which are often eaten by bobwhites and some other birds.

The eastern redbud is too small a tree to produce wood of commercial importance, but it is sometimes used locally for small turned articles or cabinet work. Usually it is no more than 15 to 20 feet in height, with a scaly-barked trunk 6 or 8 inches in diameter. Occasional trees attain a height of 40 feet, with a trunk diameter of 1 to 2 feet. A champion recorded by the American Forestry Association—a tree at Dayton, Ohio—has a branch spread of 46 feet, and its trunk is 8 feet 3 inches in circumference at 4½ feet above ground.

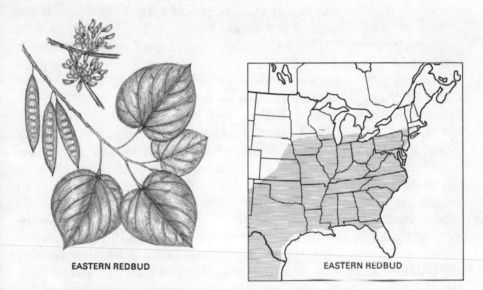

EASTERN REDBUD

EASTERN REDBUD

An Old-World cousin of the redbud has long been known as the Judas tree. According to legend, it had had white flowers until Judas Iscariot hanged himself from one of its boughs after his betrayal of Jesus; whereupon the white flowers blushed red with shame, and so they have remained ever since. The legend crossed the Atlantic with the early settlers, and the name of the Judas tree was transferred to the native species. As a matter of fact, the flowers of an occasional Eastern redbud are white instead of the usual bright pink, but such trees are rather rare. *Cercis* is the classical Greek name of the Old-World Judas tree, and *canadensis* was the name assigned by Linnaeus, who supposed the redbud to be a native of Canada.

## BLACK LOCUST (*Robinia pseudoacacia*)

The original home of the black locust is believed to have been in the Appalachian region, from southern Pennsylvania south to Georgia, and in a small area in the Ozark Mountains of southern Missouri, Arkansas, and eastern Oklahoma. Now it is so widely naturalized throughout the eastern United States and adjacent Canada that the exact boundaries of its native range will probably never be known. In many parts of the West it has been planted for windbreaks and shelterbelts; even as far west as Oregon, it has escaped from cultivation and is now growing wild. The black locust was introduced into Germany shortly after 1600, and today in Europe it is one of the most widely distributed of American trees.

In most places the black locust is a medium-sized tree from 40 to 60 feet in height, with a trunk 1 to 2 feet in diameter. On better soils that are moist and loamy, and particularly on those of limestone origin, it grows much larger—to a height of about 100 feet, with a trunk diameter of 3 feet or more. A tree near Jefferson, Indiana, with a height of 85 feet, a branch spread of 60 feet, and a trunk with a breast-high circumference of 15 feet 11 inches, is the current champion listed by the American Forestry Association. Black locusts grow rapidly, and it is doubtful whether very many attain an age of much over 100 years. In the open the tree develops an open and irregular crown.

Most black locusts bear pairs of short spines on their twigs where the stalks of the leaves are attached, although on an occasional tree they may be lacking. These spines, botanists tell us, are modified stipules, corresponding to the leaflike structures that develop at the bases of the leaf stalks of many plants. The leaves are divided into from seven to nineteen leaflets which are oval or egg-shaped, smooth-edged, dark bluish-green above, paler beneath, and an inch or two long. At some time between April and June, when the leaves are about half-grown, the tree puts forth drooping clusters of snow-white, pealike flowers which are intensely fragrant. Later the pistils of the flowers develop into narrow, flattened, pealike pods from 2 to 4 inches in length, each containing from four to eight hard brown seeds that resemble tiny beans.

As in most members of the pea family—to which the locust belongs—the roots of the black locust bear little nodules containing nitrogen-fixing bacteria, which are able to take nitrogen from the air between the soil particles and convert it into chemicals that other plants are able to assimilate. Locust trees therefore improve the soil in which they grow. Since they are able to grow on poor, dry soils, although they do not make their best growth there, black locusts are useful in reclaiming old, worn-out fields and the unsightly spoil banks that are too often left by strip miners.

Black locust wood is very heavy, hard, and resistant to decay. It has long been a favorite for fence posts, mine timbers, stakes, poles, and railroad ties, and is the principal wood used to make the insulator pins that are inserted on the cross-arms of telephone and power-line poles. Trees of a superior variety, known for generations on Long Island and adjacent parts of New York, whose tall trunks are exceptionally straight, bear the traditional name of "shipmast locusts." According to local tradition, the seedling trees were brought from Virginia by Captain John Sands at some time about 1700. In 1936 botanists finally got around to acknowledging the "shipmast locust" as a distinct variety. This variety is now known to grow in a wild state on mountain slopes in Randolph and Pocahontas counties, West Virginia.

Linnaeus gave the name *Robinia* to the genus to which the black locust belongs, in honor of Jean Robin and his son Vespasian, who were herbalists to the kings of France during the late sixteenth and early seventeenth centuries, and who first cultivated the tree in Europe. *Pseudoacacia*, an early name for the tree, means "false acacia."

## HONEY LOCUST (*Gleditsia triacanthos*)

A distinctive feature of the honey locust is the formidable array of stout, branched thorns which stud its trunk; and its branches and twigs are well armed, too. Occasionally a tree may lack this armament, but such trees are rare outside of cultivation. Distinctive, too, are the flat, strap-shaped, usually twisted, dark-brown pods which are often 12 to 18 inches in length; and so are the leaves, some of which are simply divided into from four to seven pairs of narrowly egg-shaped leaflets, which may have inconspicuous teeth on their edges. Others, however, are divided a second time into more numerous but smaller leaflets. These a botanist would describe as "doubly compound."

Honey locusts grow chiefly in low-lying woods and on their borders, along streams, and very often along roadsides and fencerows. Their original range covered a big area in the midland United States, north to the southern part of the Great Lakes region, south to the Gulf Coast states, east to the Appalachian region, west to southeastern South Dakota and thence into northeastern Texas. Today the species is often met well beyond its former range, for it has been planted widely in shelterbelts and as a shade tree.

Ordinarily the honey locust is a tree from 60 to 80 feet in height, with a trunk 2 to 3 feet in diameter, but it has been known to attain a height of

140 feet and to have a trunk diameter of as much as 6 feet. One near Queenstown, Maryland, is 92 feet tall with a branch spread of 112 feet, and at 4½ feet above the ground its trunk has a circumference of 18 feet 9 inches. According to the American Forestry Association, it is the present champion.

The flowers, which appear on the branches of the tree between April and June, are relatively inconspicuous—small, greenish-yellow or whitish in

BLACK LOCUST                    HONEY LOCUST

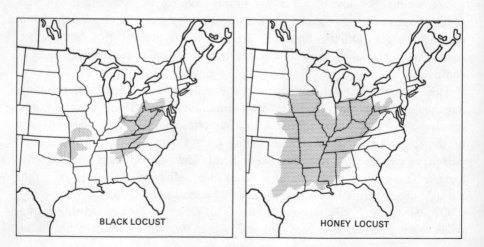

BLACK LOCUST                    HONEY LOCUST

color, and arranged in narrow clusters from 2 to 2½ inches long. They look
not at all like pea-flowers, though they are fragrant and attract many bees.
The tree gets its name, however, from the sweet and juicy pulp that surrounds the oval-shaped, beanlike seeds within the long pods. Rabbits, deer,
squirrels, and domestic cattle eat the pods for this pulp; and many a small
boy has discovered that it makes a very pleasant morsel to nibble on. In
some places the tree is commonly known as the honeyshucks.

Thornless varieties of the honey locust have long been used as shade trees,
but in recent years several new and superior forms have been developed and
patented, and may be found in any nursery catalog. Thornless and with
crowns of lacy foliage, and never producing pods like those of the wild trees,
these new varieties include the "Shademaster" and "Moraine" locusts, with
dark-green foliage, and the "Sunburst Locust," whose young leaves at the
tips of the branches are golden yellow. The latest, the "Rubylace Locust,"
has red-colored leaves.

Although the hard, strong, and durable wood of the honey locust has
little commercial importance, it is used locally for fence posts, furniture,
rough construction, and railroad ties.

The name *Gleditsia* honors Johann Gottlieb Gleditsch, who was director
of the botanical garden at Berlin, Germany, during the eighteenth century;
and *triacanthos,* meaning "three-thorned," refers to the branched thorns.


## KENTUCKY COFFEE TREE (*Gymnocladus dioicus*)

For nearly half the year a Kentucky coffee tree looks more dead than
alive. Its leaves not only appear quite late in the spring, but also turn
yellow early in the fall and soon drop to the ground. The name *Gym-
nocladus* is from the Greek, meaning "naked branch," and refers to the
stout naked branches with their heavy-looking twigs, which are a conspicuous feature of the tree during most of the year, and which the foliage is not
dense enough to conceal, even in summer.

The twigs, or smaller branchlets, are very stout, greenish-brown in color,
and commonly coated with a whitish, crusty film. They bear large, heart-
shaped, raised scars left by the shed leaves. The trunk of an open-grown tree
is usually short, dividing into a few large ascending branches which form an
irregular, rather narrow, round-topped crown. Usually the tree is from 40 to
80 feet high, with a trunk 1 to 2 feet in diameter, though occasionally it
attains a height as great as 100 feet with a trunk diameter of 3 feet or more.
The champion, according to the American Forestry Association, is a tree
near Hartford, Kentucky, which has a height of 84 feet, a branch spread of

60 feet, and a trunk circumference of 13 feet 7 inches at 4½ feet above ground.

The leaves of the Kentucky coffee tree are from 1 to 3 feet long, and often 2 feet in width. They are divided twice, first into stalks, which in turn are divided into several egg-shaped, pointed leaflets from 2 to 2½ inches in length; but usually, at the base of the leaf, there is a pair of solitary and somewhat larger leaflets. The individual leaflets into which the leaf is divided often number fifty or more.

About June the tree may produce greenish-white flowers, which are not at all pealike, though the tree is a member of the pea family. The flower clusters are 3 or 4 inches long, and the stamen-bearing and pistil-bearing flowers grow on separate trees. The name *dioicus* refers to the flowers; it

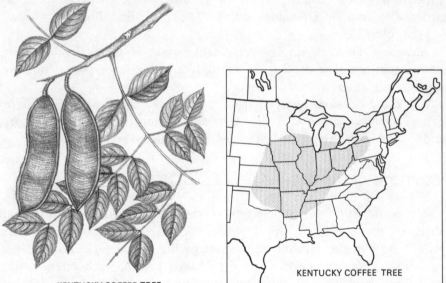

KENTUCKY COFFEE TREE

KENTUCKY COFFEE TREE

means "in two households." By fall the pistil-bearing trees carry thick, flattened, purplish-brown pods from 6 to 10 inches long and 1 to 2 inches broad. Each pod contains half a dozen or more flattened, round, dark-brown seeds, more than ½ inch across, and surrounded by a sticky pulp. These pods often persist on the trees far into the winter.

The seeds, according to the botanical explorer François André Michaux, were used by "the early immigrants to Kentucky and Tennessee, who hoped to find in its seeds a substitute for coffee; but the small number of persons who made the experiment abandoned it, as soon as it became easy to obtain from seaports the coffee of the West Indies." Evidently these early settlers gave the Kentucky coffee tree its name. The Indians are said to have roasted the large seeds and eaten them like chestnuts.

The natural range of the Kentucky coffee tree is supposed to have extended from western New York and extreme southern Ontario to southeastern South Dakota, and southward to central Tennessee, Arkansas, and western Oklahoma. The species usually grows in rich, moist bottomlands, but within most of its range it is rather rare and local in occurrence. It has been quite widely planted, well beyond its original range, and seems actually to be much more common in cultivation than in the wild state. Its durable wood is little used, except locally for fence posts and railroad ties.

## BLUE PALOVERDE (*Cercidium floridum*)

During the greater part of the year the blue paloverde is a leafless, short-trunked, green-barked, thorny little tree from about 15 to 30 feet in height. Its trunk rarely measures as much as 20 inches in diameter, and is often crooked or inclined at an angle; and near the bases of larger trees the bark may become seamed and scaly, and turn a reddish-brown. But in late April or early May the scraggly paloverde is suddenly transformed by a blaze of shimmering, bright-yellow, five-petaled flowers—each one about an inch across and with its uppermost petal red-spotted—that literally cover the tree. In flower, it is indeed one of the most beautiful trees of the desert and the desert foothills.

The leaves of the paloverde are tiny and fleeting. They appear on the branchlets when the tree comes into bloom, and often long before autumn the last of them is gone. Each one is an inch or a trifle more long, with two or three pairs of little, oval-shaped, dull-green leaflets. As is usual in desert-inhabiting plants, the green bark of the tree's trunk and branches takes over the food-making function usually performed by leaves. By midsummer the beanlike pods, 2 to 3 inches long, mature and turn yellow; each one contains two or three large seeds.

The blue paloverde is found from southern and central Arizona west to southeastern California, and southward into northwestern Mexico. From near sea level to elevations of 3,500 feet it clings to the sides of desert canyons and dry washes. It grows in depressions in the arid sandhills and on the lower foothills of the desert country. The name paloverde—which means "green tree"—was given by the Spaniards who explored the American West in their quest for the legendary Seven Cities of Cibola, whose streets were supposed to have been paved with gold.

Arizona—where the tree with the golden blossoms grows so profusely—has made the blue paloverde its state tree. The pale-yellowish-brown wood is heavy but soft and brittle, and has little if any commercial value. Nectar from the flowers is the source of a good honey, and the seeds have been a staple food of the southwestern Indians. While still green they are eaten like lima beans, and when dried they are ground into meal. Cattle will browse on the branchlets of the paloverde only when nothing more palatable can be found. The greatest service rendered by the tree today is in slowing down the erosion of the soil.

*Cercidium,* the Latinized form of a Greek word meaning "weaver's comb," refers to the fancied resemblance of the pods to such an object, and *floridum* means "full of flowers."

BLUE PALOVERDE

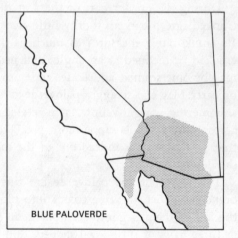

BLUE PALOVERDE

# BURSERA FAMILY

## GUMBO LIMBO (*Bursera simaruba*)

🌺 ANYONE traveling southward along either coast of Florida—from Cape Canaveral on the east coast or from Tampa Bay on the west—will sooner or later meet the gumbo limbo. A tropical American tree, it is found also in the West Indies, where it is called the West Indian birch, as well as in Mexico, Central America, and northern South America. In Florida it regularly sheds its leaves during the winter, but at any season of the year it may be recognized by the smooth and oily appearance of the bark on its trunk and larger branches.

The gumbo limbo is a round-topped tree 50 to 60 feet in height, with a short trunk most often 2 to 3 feet in diameter. According to the American Forestry Association, the champion is a tree in Fairchild Gardens, South Miami, Florida with a height of 45 feet, a limb spread of 61 feet, and a trunk 6 feet 8 inches in circumference at 4½ feet above the ground.

The bark of both the trunk and the larger branches is glandular-dotted or resinous, and peels freely into thin, papery, bright-reddish-brown scales,

GUMBO LIMBO

GUMBO LIMBO

which fall off to expose the dark-reddish-brown-to-gray bark underneath. The alternate leaves are crowded toward the ends of the stout, crooked branchlets. Each one is divided into from three to seven, but usually five, somewhat leathery, dark-green leaflets which are from 1 to 3 inches in length. The leaflets are smooth-edged, pointed at the tip, and somewhat uneven at the base.

In winter or spring, before the new leaves appear or just as they are unfolding, tiny greenish flowers are borne in erect clusters from 2 to 5 inches long, stamen-bearing and pistil-bearing both on the same tree. The fruits, which mature in summer, are less than ½ inch long. They have a thick, dark-red, three-angled outer coat which separates into three sections, exposing the usually solitary, rose-colored, bony seed.

The gumbo limbo is an interesting tree although it is of no commercial importance. İts wood is soft and spongy, light in weight, and weak. Fence posts made of the green logs have been known to take root and grow rapidly into trees, but the dried wood quickly decays. In the West Indies the aromatic resin that flows from cuts made in the trunk is made into a varnish, and the leaves are said to be a usable substitute for tea.

The name *Bursera* honors Joachim Burser, a German botanist and physician who lived from 1593 to 1649, and *simaruba* is a name applied by the Carib Indians to another tree.

# HOLLY FAMILY

## AMERICAN HOLLY (*Ilex opaca*)

❧ ENGLISH colonists who settled along the Atlantic seaboard were delighted to find in the forests of the New World a holly quite similar to the one which had long contributed to the festivities of the Christmas season at home. The leaves were not quite so glossy a dark green, and its berries not so bright a red, as those of the English holly. But here in the American wilderness this tree—the American holly—made a most acceptable substitute, and it was indeed welcome. And since Colonial times the American holly has been connected with the celebration of Christmas—so much so that it has disappeared from many of the places where it once grew.

The American holly is found along the Atlantic coast from Massachusetts south to central Florida, and westward through the Ohio Valley to Missouri, southeastern Oklahoma, and eastern Texas. Usually scattered individuals occur in damp to well-drained woodlands, but occasionally the tree forms

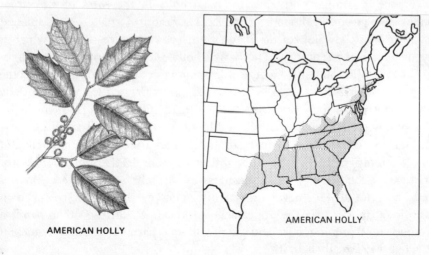

AMERICAN HOLLY

AMERICAN HOLLY

small pure stands. In the southeastern states it grows from the coastal regions inland to the mountains, commonly reaching elevations between 3,000 and 4,000 feet; but Arthur Stupka has found it at altitudes up to 4,250 and 4,900 feet in Great Smoky Mountains National Park.

In the coastal region of Massachusetts the American holly is hardly more than a shrub, but southward it becomes a medium-sized to large tree. Commonly it may be 40 to 60 feet high, with a trunk 1 to 2 feet in diameter. Occasionally it has attained a height as much as 100 feet, with a trunk diameter as great as 4 feet. A champion recorded by the American Forestry Association—a tree near Hardin in Liberty County, Texas—has a height of 53 feet, a branch spread of 61 feet, and a trunk measuring 13 feet 4 inches in circumference at 4½ feet above the ground.

Sometime between April and June, depending on latitude and altitude, the tree produces small clusters or solitary, little, four-petaled, greenish-white flowers, which are fragrant and attract swarms of bees. On some trees all the flowers contain only pollen-producing stamens, while other trees have only pistils. This explains why some holy trees never produce berries. Nurserymen refer to the trees with stamen-bearing flowers as male trees, and those with pistil-bearing flowers as female trees. Of course, if a female tree is to produce a crop of berries there must be at least one male tree in the neighborhood. Bees carry the pollen between the two, and thus pollinate the flowers of the female trees. Holly berries, by the way, are not true berries. A botanist will tell you, rather, that they are drupes containing a few large and bony nutlets. Sometimes a tree will bear yellow fruits instead of the usual red ones.

Everyone is familiar with the American holly in the form of Christmas wreaths and greens, and some know it as a beautiful shade or ornamental tree. It grows slowly and reaches maturity in 100 to 150 years, after which it may live for many centuries. The native holly was a favorite tree throughout Colonial Virginia, and George Washington confided to his diary some of his experiences with it. He discovered, as many gardeners have done since, that it is not the easiest tree to transplant successfully from the wild. But some of the hollies he planted at Mount Vernon are still standing.

In far too many places, American holly trees have been mutilated and even wantonly destroyed by thoughtless persons gathering boughs for Christmas decorations. This carelessness is entirely unwarranted. Boughs should be carefully cut, never broken off, and they should not be taken in quantities that will mar the appearance of the tree. On the other hand, a little judicious pruning now and then will not harm a prized ornamental holly, but may actually help it.

Aside from its ornamental value, the American holly produces an excellent wood. Both the heartwood and the sapwood are white, the former with an ivory cast. Holly wood is heavy and hard though not very strong, and has a uniform and compact texture. In addition, it is readily penetrable by liquids and thus is easily dyed. Because of these qualities it is used principally for making scientific and musical instruments, furniture inlays, and various athletic goods. The black keys on a piano are most commonly made from holly wood.

*Ilex* is the classical Latin name for the holm oak of Europe, which has hollylike leaves, and *opaca,* meaning "opaque" or "dark," refers to the rather dull green of the leaves.

# MAPLE FAMILY

❧ MAPLES are among the few groups of trees which have opposite leaves—that is, leaves arranged in pairs and placed directly across from each other on the branchlets. Usually, too, their leaves are palmately lobed and long-stalked; so if a tree has opposite leaves that are lobed, one can be reasonably certain that it is a maple. A few maples, however, have leaves which are compound, with leaflets placed along a stalk and with an odd one at the end. If fruits happen to be present, all doubt will be dispelled as to whether or not the tree is a maple. Maple fruits are always borne in pairs. The seed-bearing portions at the base are joined together, and each one is tipped with a long wing. These fruits are called "keys," and are as typical of maples as acorns are of oaks.

Although the flowers of maples are never very large, they often occur in clusters that make them conspicuous. Each flower has a calyx that is usually five-parted, and some maple flowers may also have five small petals. There are a number of stamens, and usually some of the flowers in each cluster have a pistil as well. The flowers of some maples appear in late winter or early spring before the leaves develop; in others they are borne at the same time.

Several kinds of maples from abroad are often planted in America as shade or ornamental trees. The most familiar of these is the Norway maple (*Acer platanoides*), which is widely planted as both a shade and a street tree. This maple is most often confused with our native sugar maple, since the two have leaves somewhat similar in shape. A quick determination can be made when the leaves are present. If a drop of milky sap appears when the leaf stalk is broken, the tree is definitely a Norway maple.

About 115 species of maples are found in the Northern Hemisphere, and about a dozen of these are native to various parts of North America.

*Acer* is the classical Latin name for a maple tree.

## SUGAR MAPLE (*Acer saccharum*)

The first English colonists were surprised to learn that the Indians made sugar from the sap of certain trees that grew in the forests of the New World. The English chemist Robert Boyle was likewise so impressed that he announced the fact to the learned men of Europe as a major scientific discovery. Although the Indians used the sap of several kinds of trees for this purpose, one tree was outstanding, and it came to be called the sugar maple. The scientific name *saccharum* means "sugar," and refers to the sweetish sap.

Sugar maples grow from the southern tip of Newfoundland and Nova Scotia westward through southern Quebec and Ontario to Minnesota, and southward in the Appalachian region to Georgia and to northeastern Texas. Wherever it grows it is an outstanding feature of the landscape, especially in the fall, when the leaves turn a brilliant yellow or orange flushed with red. Few trees match the glorious autumn coloration of the sugar maple as it is found in New England, the Lake States, and the coves of the Appalachian mountains.

Commonly the tree attains a height of 60 to 80 feet, with a trunk 2 to 3 feet in diameter, but an occasional sugar maple has been as much as 135 feet tall, with a trunk diameter exceeding 5 feet. The present champion listed by the American Forestry Association is a tree in Garrett County, Maryland, with a height of 116 feet, a limb spread of 75 feet, and a trunk measuring 19 feet 9 inches in circumference at 4½ feet above the ground. Another tree, in the Great Smoky Mountains National Park, has a trunk circumference of 15 feet 4 inches. Open-grown trees have a relatively short trunk and a dense, rounded, or dome-shaped crown. In the forest the trunks are clear of branches for some distance above the ground.

The leaves of the sugar maple usually have five long-pointed and sparingly wavy-toothed lobes. They are bright-green above, paler below, and measure from 3 to 5 inches across. At some time between April and June, clusters of greenish-yellow flowers on hairy, threadlike stalks appear on the branchlets; and sometimes they are so numerous that the trees seem to be enveloped in a yellowish haze. By midsummer or early autumn the pairs of fruits, or keys, mature; each pair somewhat resembles a horseshoe in shape.

The sugar maple is popular as a shade and street tree, and it is also an important timber tree. The wood is heavy, hard, and strong, and has a fine and uniform texture. Lumbermen know it as "hard maple." Since colonial days it has been used for making fine furniture, and as flooring it ranks among the best. Its many other uses include agricultural implements, shoe lasts, handles, woodenware and novelties, spools and bobbins, boxes and crates. Occasional trees have a contorted grain, the "curly" or "bird's-eye maple" much sought after by cabinet-makers, and for making gunstocks and the backs of violins. Various chemicals are also produced from the wood by distillation.

Maple sugar and syrup are made by tapping the trees in late winter or early spring, before the buds begin to swell. The sap is collected and boiled in a large kettle or in an evaporator until it reaches the proper consistency. From thirty to thirty-five gallons of sap are usually required to make a gallon of maple syrup. About four gallons, on an average, will yield one pound of sugar. In groves of sugar maples, buckets are hung from little metal spouts which have been inserted into holes bored into the trunks of the trees. As the buckets fill with sap they are emptied into a barrel on a low sled, usually drawn by horses, in which the sap is then carried to the boiling house and poured into the evaporator, a mechanism so constructed that sap poured into one end flows slowly to the other, boiling rapidly along the way. By the time it reaches the lower end it is of the right consistency for syrup, and it is drawn off and poured into cans.

This is the way maple syrup has been made for generations, and the way it is still made in most places; but in other, ultra-modernized groves the sap now flows from tree to evaporator through a system of plastic pipes. The new way is undoubtedly more efficient, but it lacks the romance long associated with the old method. To many simply the mention of maple syrup or sugar brings back pleasant memories of the rhythmical dripping of sap into the buckets, the all-night vigil around the foaming pan, the fragrance of wood smoke mingled with that of sweetish steam, and finally the moment of "sugaring-off," when some of the hot syrup was poured into the snow, where it thickened into a delicious taffy.

Lacking metal vessels in which to boil down the sap, Northern Indians collected it in buckets made of birch bark. Then they poured it into a trough made from the hollowed-out section of a tree trunk, and boiled it down by putting heated rocks into the trough. Another method used by the Indians was to allow the sap to freeze repeatedly, removing the ice at each freezing. Gradually the sap thickened until it acquired the consistency of syrup.

When maple sugar was first made by the early settlers, commercial sugars as we know them today were unknown, since the processes of crystallizing and refining sugar lay far in the future. Thus in pioneer days, and for a long time thereafter, maple sugar was a staple food. When commercial sugars finally made their appearance, the demand for maple sugar did not diminish appreciably. It simply changed status, from a staple food to a table delicacy.

New York, Vermont, West Virginia, and Wisconsin have all made the sugar maple their state tree; and all four states are among the top producers of maple syrup and maple sugar.

## BIGLEAF MAPLE (*Acer macrophyllum*)

The bigleaf maple is the king of Pacific coast maples, and it is one of the few commercially important hardwood trees of the region. It is found from Alaska south into southern California, usually scattered or in small groves; but it attains its best growth and greatest importance in the river bottoms of Oregon and Washington, where the trees are often 100 feet tall, with trunks 3 to 4 feet in diameter and free of branches for half or more of their length. The champion listed by the American Forestry Association—a tree near Portland, Oregon—has a trunk 23 feet 6 inches in circumference at 4½ feet above the ground, and a height of 96 feet. In the open the bigleaf maple develops a broadly rounded head and a short trunk, and usually ranges between 50 and 75 feet in height.

The tree gets both its common name and the scientific name *macrophyllum* from its large leaves, which are 6 inches to a foot wide—larger than those of any other American maple. Usually they are deeply five-lobed, and the lobes generally have a few large teeth or additional smaller lobes. On the upper surface they are a shiny dark-green, and the lower surface is paler. In autumn they turn a clear yellow or bright orange, adding a touch of brilliant color to the prevailing green of the coniferous forest.

In April or May, after the leaves are fully developed, large drooping clusters of fragrant yellow flowers appear on many of the branchlets. Stamen-bearing and pistil-bearing flowers are present on the same tree, and by fall the latter become pairs of winged fruits or "keys," from 1½ to 2 inches long. They are tawny or yellowish-brown when ripe, and they often remain on the trees until mid-winter or later. The basal portion of the fruit, which contains the seed, is covered with sharp bristlelike hairs.

During its first 40 to 60 years a bigleaf maple grows quite rapidly, but after that the growth slows down. A tree reaches maturity at between 200 and 300 years. Old trees often have large burls on their trunks and produce a wood with a wavy or curly grain that is highly prized by manufacturers of furniture and novelties. Bigleaf maple wood is comparable in quality to that of the eastern sugar maple.

## RED MAPLE (*Acer rubrum*)

At almost any season of the year there will be something red about a red maple. In winter it has lustrous dark-red twigs on which are clustered the brighter, almost blood-red buds. Then, in late winter or early spring, the buds open into flowers which are occasionally yellow but usually bright red; and a little later come the bright red fruits. All summer long the stalks of the leaves are red; and in fall the leaves, though sometimes they may be yellow, usually turn a most brilliant red—which is what the scientific name *rubrum* means.

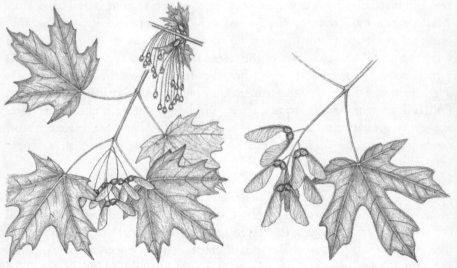

SUGAR MAPLE                    BIGLEAF MAPLE

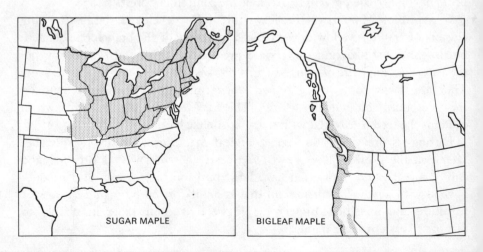

SUGAR MAPLE          BIGLEAF MAPLE

**RED MAPLE**

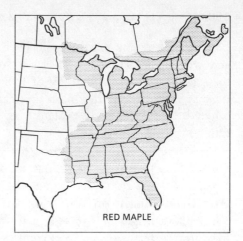

RED MAPLE

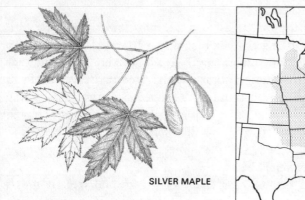

**SILVER MAPLE**

SILVER MAPLE

**ASH-LEAVED MAPLE**

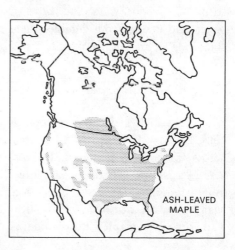

ASH-LEAVED
MAPLE

Red maples grow practically all over the eastern half of the United States and well up into Canada. They are found in the swampy lowlands along the coast and almost to the tops of the southern Appalachians. Over most of its vast range this is the most abundant of the maples. Rhode Island has selected the red maple as its state tree, and the maple leaf is the emblem of Canada.

As a rule the red maple grows to a height of 50 to 70 feet, with a trunk from 1 to 2 feet in diameter; but an occasional tree may attain a height of 120 feet, with a trunk diameter up to about 5 feet. The American Forestry Association's champion is a tree near Utica, Macomb County, Michigan, which has a height of 136 feet, a limb spread of 95 feet, and a trunk that measures 15 feet 4 inches in circumference at 4½ feet above ground. In the Greenbrier area of Great Smoky Mountains National Park, another tree has a trunk 17 feet 3 inches in circumference.

Red maples are among the first trees to come into flower. At lower altitudes in the South, they often begin to bloom as early as January. In the higher mountains they may not bloom until April or even May, but they always do so long before the leaves appear. By the time the leaves begin to expand, the fruits are mature and stand in V-shaped pairs waiting for the winds to carry them away. The leaves usually have three short-pointed lobes, sometimes with another pair of smaller lobes toward the base, and they are also irregularly toothed. On the upper surface they are a bright light-green, and they are whitened below.

The red maple is often planted as a shade or ornamental tree. It grows quite rapidly and attains maturity in about 70 or 80 years. In many respects its wood resembles that of the sugar maple, except that it is not nearly so hard or strong, and lumbermen usually call it "soft maple." It is used for furniture, woodenware and novelties, handles, spools and bobbins, and boxes and crates. Considerable quantities are used in making charcoal and chemicals, or are sent to paper mills as pulpwood.

## SILVER MAPLE (*Acer saccharinum*)

Silver maples grow in bottomlands and along the banks of streams from New Brunswick westward through southern Ontario, Michigan, and Minnesota to southeastern South Dakota, and southward to northwestern Florida, Mississippi, Arkansas, and northeastern Oklahoma. Nowhere are they more abundant, however, than along the Ohio and its tributary streams. Many who are not acquainted with the tree in its native haunts know it well, for silver maples are planted as shade or street trees in virtually every city and town within its natural range and even beyond it.

In the open the silver maple has a grayish-barked trunk which divides near the ground into several large ascending limbs. The lower branches sweep gracefully downward and turn up at the tips, the middle branches spread horizontally, and the upper ones ascend to form a broadly rounded crown. Commonly the silver maple is a tree 60 to 80 feet in height with a trunk 2 to 3 feet in diameter, but sometimes it may attain a height of 120 feet, with a trunk diameter as great as 5 feet. The current champion listed by the American Forestry Association—a tree at Fryeburg-Harbor, Maine—has a height of 90 feet, a branch spread of 110 feet, and a trunk circumference of 22 feet 10 inches at 4½ feet above the ground.

During the first warm days of late winter or early spring, the buds on the winter twigs begin to open, and dense clusters of little greenish-yellow flowers appear. Those with stamens and those with pistils may occur on the same tree or on separate trees. By the time the leafy shoots have emerged from their buds, the slender-stalked pairs of fruits with wide-spreading wings are mature and are waiting to be scattered by the winds.

In summer a silver maple may be known by its leaves, which are bright-green above and silvery-white below. They are deeply cut into five lobes, which in turn are sharply and irregularly toothed, and the sides of the topmost lobe always slope inward. As the leaves stand on slender stalks, even the slightest breeze causes them to turn over and show their silvery undersides. In fall they turn yellow before being shed for the winter.

Although it is attractive, the silver maple's principal advantage as a shade tree is its rapid growth. A big disadvantage is that the limbs and branches are so brittle that they are likely to be broken by high winds or ice storms. When this happens, wood-destroying fungi readily enter the wounds and decay sets in, so that many larger trees often have hollow trunks. As a timber tree the silver maple is of relatively minor importance. Lumbermen call the wood "soft maple," and it goes to market as such along with that of the red maple. Its sap yields a good quality of syrup and sugar, but has a lower sugar content than the sugar maple. The scientific name *saccharinum*, meaning "sweet" or "sugary," refers to the sap.

## ASH-LEAVED MAPLE (*Acer negundo*)

Among American maples the ash-leaved maple—or box elder, as it is often called—is unique in having compound leaves. Its paired leaves are divided into from three to five, or more rarely seven or nine leaflets. Each leaflet is 2 to 4 inches in length, long-pointed at the tip, coarsely toothed or sometimes three-lobed. In summer the leaves are bright-green, but they turn yellow in fall. During April or May, usually when the leaf buds are opening, clusters of little greenish-yellow flowers appear from other buds along the twigs. Later in the year, pairs of V-shaped winged fruits or keys mature on the trees that produced pistil-bearing flowers. They are borne in loose drooping clusters, and often remain on the trees long after the leaves have been shed.

The ash-leaved maple is found along streams and the borders of lakes throughout much of the United States and southern Canada. It grows abundantly along the Mississippi and all of its tributary streams, and is one of the few trees encountered by early settlers in the prairie region of the West. Usually a small tree, it may attain a height of 40 or 50 feet, with a trunk diameter of 2 to 3 feet, and occasionally one is much larger. The American Forestry Association reports a champion from Spring Brook State Park in Ohio, with a height of 81 feet, a branch spread of 108 feet, and a trunk circumference of 13 feet 6 inches at 4½ feet above the ground.

As a timber tree this maple is of no great commercial importance. Its wood—which is the lightest of all American maples—is occasionally used for cheap furniture, woodenware, boxes, and crates. Once the box elder was widely planted as a shade or street tree, but it is no longer popular. Although it grows rapidly, it is comparatively short-lived. Its brittle branches are so often broken by ice and winds that usually it does not have a very attractive form. The sap makes an excellent sugar, and in the plains and prairie regions of the West the ash-leaved maple is the chief source of maple syrup and sugar. Practically every year it fruits abundantly, and its seeds are a favorite food of the evening grosbeak and some other birds.

The scientific name *negundo* comes from the Sanskrit name of an Oriental shrub, and was applied by Linnaeus to this species of maple.

# HORSECHESTNUT FAMILY

## YELLOW BUCKEYE (*Aesculus octandra*)

❦  BUCKEYES are the only native North American trees having compound leaves with leaflets radiating from the summit of a long leaf stalk like the spokes of a wheel. Their leaves are borne in pairs, one opposite the other on the twig. When the leaves are shed in autumn, they leave large scars on the twig, which usually has a big bud at the tip. Buckeyes get their name from the large, lustrous brown seed which has a big paler-colored scar, although to see the resemblance to the eye of a buck, or male deer, requires a bit of imagination. The seeds contain a poisonous substance, and should never be eaten; carrying one in a pocket to ward off rheumatism, as some superstitious people do, is harmless though not very effective. Each large leathery capsule usually contains one seed, or sometimes two.

The yellow buckeye, the largest American species, occurs in the Ohio Valley from western Pennsylvania west to Illinois, and southward in the Appalachian region to Georgia and Alabama. It is usually a tree 40 to 60

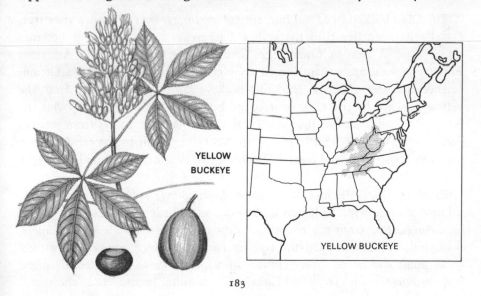

YELLOW
BUCKEYE

YELLOW BUCKEYE

feet in height, with a trunk 1 to 2 feet in diameter. The best development and greatest size are attained in the rich coves of the southern Appalachian Mountains, where trees up to 90 feet tall and with trunks 2 to 4 feet in diameter are not unusual. Along the trail from Cherokee Orchard to Trillium Gap in Great Smoky Mountains National Park is a champion tree, with a height of 85 feet and a trunk 15 feet 11 inches in circumference at 4½ feet above the ground. Arthur Stupka, who for many years was the park naturalist, measured another in Cade's Cove which had a circumference of 14 feet, and one just south of Chimney Tops is approximately 100 feet high with a trunk 15 feet 9 inches in circumference.

In April or May the yellow buckeye produces creamy-white to yellowish or occasionally reddish flowers in narrow, upright end clusters. By August the smooth, leathery capsules, often 2 inches broad, become mature and split open to release their big seeds or "buckeyes." The leaves usually have five elliptical leaflets which are from 4 to about 6 inches in length, with finely toothed edges, pointed tips, and tapering bases.

The wood of all the buckeyes is soft, weak, rather light, and whitish to pale yellowish in color. It is used to make artificial limbs, dishes, bowls, furniture, boxes and crates. The early settlers often planed it into long shavings, which they used to make "chip" hats. Today some buckeye wood is made into veneer, and it also goes to paper mills as pulpwood.

*Aesculus* is the classical Latin name for an oak or other mast-producing tree; *octandra,* meaning "with eight stamens," refers to the flowers.

The Ohio buckeye, or fetid buckeye (*Aesculus glabra*) is Ohio's state tree. Usually it is smaller than the yellow buckeye but occasionally it becomes quite large. A tree in Champaign County, Ohio, which is the American Forestry Association's champion, is 85 feet tall, and its trunk has a circumference of 9 feet 9 inches. The Ohio buckeye can be distinguished from the yellow buckeye by the rank odor of its bruised leaves or broken twigs, by its spiny capsules, and by the keeled scales of its buds. It grows from western Pennsylvania to Iowa and southeastern Nebraska, south to central Alabama, northern Mississippi, and central Oklahoma. *Glabra* means "smooth."

Familiar, too, is the introduced horse chestnut (*Aesculus hippocastanum*), a European tree widely planted in America as a shade and street tree. It can be distinguished from the native buckeyes by its leaves with seven leaflets, which are broadest toward the tip; by its buds, which are coated with a sticky gum; and by its showy clusters of white flowers. The scientific name *hippocastanum* comes from two Latin words meaning "horse" and "chestnut."

# LINDEN FAMILY

## AMERICAN BASSWOOD (*Tilia americana*)

AS a group the basswoods are readily distinguished from other native trees. They have more or less heart-shaped, alternate leaves which are very much lopsided at the base and have saw-toothed margins. In summer, the little, creamy-white flowers are grouped on a long stalk which seems to arise from the midrib of a strap-shaped leaf or bract; and these flowers are followed by hard, roundish little fruits. Even in winter the basswoods may be known by their zig-zag twigs, along which are plump buds about as lopsided as the leaves, and covered with two or three scales. The main difficulty comes in trying to distinguish one species of basswood from another; even the best informed botanists are not sure how many species grow in our eastern forests.

In this country most people call trees of this genus basswoods, but in other parts of the world they are usually called lindens or lime trees. In this country, too, they are sometimes referred to as lindens, and in the southern Appalachians one may often hear them simply called "linns." The scientific name *Tilia* is the classical Latin name for a linden.

The American basswood, at any rate, is a common and familiar tree in forests stretching from New Brunswick and Maine westward to Manitoba, and southward into North Carolina, Tennessee, Missouri, and eastern Kansas. It is often 70 to 80 feet in height, with a trunk 2 to 3 feet in diameter, although occasionally a tree will be as much as 125 feet high, with a trunk diameter of 4 or 5 feet. According to the American Forestry Association, the champion is a tree at Queenstown, Maryland, with a height of 103 feet, a branch spread of 103 feet, and a trunk circumference of 17 feet 1 inch at 4½ feet above the ground.

In summer the American basswood bears broadly heart-shaped leaves, 4 to 8 inches long, and smooth except for occasional tufts of down in the axils of the mail veins on the lower surface. The upper surfaces are a dark but rather dull green; the under surfaces are paler. In fall the leaves turn a rather dingy yellow before being shed for the winter.

In June or July the trees are sometimes laden with white or creamy-white flowers, which are so fragrant that their presence is evident at a great distance. Bees come from far and wide to gather their nectar, so that there is a constant humming about the blossoming trees. Basswood honey is light in color and of a very high quality, with a slightly more acid tang than clover honey.

By fall the flowers have been replaced by little, hard, grayish fruits about the size and shape of garden peas. Squirrels and chipmunks often nibble into them to get at the one or two seeds inside. When the fruits are mature, the leafy bracts to which they are attached break loose and go spinning away in the winds, carrying their cargo with them.

AMERICAN BASSWOOD

Basswoods have a creamy-white to pale yellowish-brown wood that is soft, light, and easily worked. Since when dry it has no odor or taste, it is an ideal wood for making food containers. It is also used for venetian blinds, furniture, millwork, apiary supplies, woodenware, boxes and crates, veneer, and excelsior, and as pulpwood.

Like most other basswoods, this species makes a very fine shade or street tree, and it adapts itself well to city conditions. It grows quite rapidly and attains maturity in from 90 to 140 years. In the open it develops a narrow, compact, but very symmetrical crown. Sprouts grow freely from the stump of a tree that has been cut down, so that it is not unusual to see several trees growing in a clump. Old trees commonly have hollow trunks, which provide nesting space and a place of refuge for many wild creatures of the forest.

## WHITE BASSWOOD (*Tilia heterophylla*)

The white basswood is best distinguished from the American basswood by the whitened or tawny and often felted undersides of its leaves. Although found from New York and the Ohio Valley southward, it is most common in the southern Appalachians and the piedmont region. Visitors to Great Smoky Mountains National Park will find it common there to an elevation of about 5,000 feet. One along the Porters Creek Trail in the Greenbrier area of the park has a trunk measuring 11 feet 7 inches in circumference. The American Forestry Association's champion is a tree near Little Switzerland, in the mountains of western North Carolina, with a height of 80 feet, a branch spread of 61 feet, and a trunk circumference of 13 feet 9 inches at 4½ feet above the ground.

The scientific name *heterophylla,* meaning "various-leaved," perhaps refers to the usually whitened undersides of the leaves.

AMERICAN BASSWOOD

# CACTUS FAMILY

## SAGUARO (*Cereus giganteus*)

❦ KING of the cacti is the saguaro (pronounced sa-*wahr*-ro), the giant cactus of the Sonoran Desert of Arizona, adjoining Mexico, and extreme southeastern California. The columnlike stems of this tree cactus tower 20 to 60 feet in height, and the great branches look like stout arms uplifted to the sky. The stems are often a foot or two in diameter, and the branches are almost as thick. Both have deep longitudinal furrows and rounded ridges, which are armed with needle-sharp spines. There are no leaves from which precious moisture might escape into the dry desert air, and the great green stems and branches have taken over the food-making role that is usually performed by the leaves.

One might logically expect such giant cacti to be anchored in the earth by an enormous taproot, and to have a widespreading system of feeder roots; but they do no such thing. It has been determined that a fully branched specimen 50 feet tall may have only a dozen or so small lateral roots, that these may be only 10 or 12 feet long, and that the tap root is seldom more than 3 feet deep. Rainfall in the desert where the saguaro grows totals at most only about 10 inches a year, and it never penetrates very deeply into the ground. When the rains fall, the roots of the saguaro soak up water, and the whole tree expands. As much as 250 gallons of water may be absorbed by a 50-foot cactus after a single rain. When the water stored within it is used up, the whole tree shrinks and its skin becomes wrinkled.

Within the trunk and branches are a skeleton of woody ribs and a mesh-like network of woody strands, but most of the interior is soft and spongy. The wood of the saguaro is light but very hard and strong, and it is very durable. Long after the soft parts of a saguaro have decayed, its woody skeleton usually remains intact. For centuries the Southwestern Indians have used its ribs as the framework of their shelters. Fences, and the rafters of ranch houses, have been made of them, too.

After the rainy season, usually in late April or May, big, beautiful, creamy-white flowers appear on the tips of the stems and branches of the saguaro. The flowers are rimmed with numerous fragile, waxy-looking, lily-like petals, and just within these are a vastly greater number of stamens with golden anthers. In the very center is a pistil whose numerous style branches are sticky along their inner surfaces. Single flowers open during the night and are gone by the next morning, but the procession of bloom lasts over several days. Arizona has chosen the saguaro as its state flower.

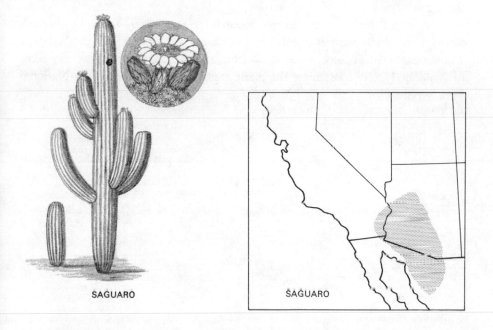

SAGUARO                    SAGUARO

Beautiful though its blooms are, the fruits of the saguaro are of more importance to desert dwellers. They are relished by many wild creatures, and they have always been gathered in large quantities by desert Indians. To harvest them, the Indians use long poles made of the saguaro's own woody rods; and the fruits are eaten raw, dried, or made into syrups, and preserves by the Indian women. Egg-shaped and about 2½ inches long, the fruits are light red when ripe. They often split open while still on the tree, disclosing a watermelon-red pulp containing numerous little, dark-brown seeds.

The Sonoran Desert is a closely knit community dominated by the saguaro and other cacti, but containing a variety of other trees and shrubs— virtually all of them bristling with spines or thorns. The desert is the home of the collared peccary of "javelina," badger, desert gray fox, desert tortoise, roadrunner, and white-winged dove. Gila woodpeckers and gilded flickers excavate nesting holes in the trunks or arms of the saguaro, and often these holes are later appropriated by other birds, including the elf owl, which is no larger than a sparrow. After a nesting hole is excavated, the sap dries and forms a hard coating on the walls, making a durable hollow vessel that lasts for years after the cactus has fallen and rotted away. Indians often gather these and use them as containers for storing the preserved or dried fruits of the saguaro.

A saguaro forest is a strange yet beautiful place, utterly unlike any other. Perhaps the finest such forest is the one preserved in the Saguaro National Monument near Tucson, Arizona. Within its boundaries, over 63,000 acres of Sonoran Desert containing the giant cactus are protected by the National Park Service.

# SOURGUM FAMILY

## BLACK GUM (*Nyssa sylvatica*)

❧ ALL the way from dry rocky ridges and mountain slopes to lowland swamps and stream bottoms, the black gum may be found. It grows in forests and woodlots, along fencerows and roadsides; and it soon invades cut-over or burned-over forest land and abandoned fields. One variety—which is distinguished by its very narrow leaves—even wades into coastal swamps and pineland ponds, often keeping company with the pond cypress, which it imitates in the swollen bases of its trunks. Few trees are less exacting than the black gum in their choice of habitat.

In most places the black gum is a small or medium-sized tree, commonly 25 to 40 feet in height, with a trunk from 1 to 2 feet in diameter; but in rich, moist bottomlands it may attain a height of 100 feet and a trunk diameter of as much as 5 feet. A champion listed by the American Forestry Association—a tree near Urania, Louisiana—has a height of 130 feet, a limb spread of 100 feet, and a trunk circumference of 15 feet 9 inches at 4½ feet above the ground. A tree in Noyubee National Wildlife Refuge, Brooksville, Mississippi, equals it in height and trunk girth but has a spread of only 65 feet.

The trunk of a black gum commonly extends undivided to the top of the tree. There are many side branches, which are mostly horizontal, although those that are uppermost tend to ascend while the lower ones often droop. As a tree grows older the top often dies, and it develops a rather flat-topped crown. On the trunks of older trees the bark becomes deeply broken into irregular but more or less rectangular blocks, whose appearance suggests an alligator's hide.

In summer the black gum has dark-green, smooth-edged leaves which are shiny on the upper side, usually broadest above the middle, pointed at both ends, and from 2 to 5 inches long. In fall they turn a brilliant blood-red, often beginning before the end of August, while other trees are still green.

By autumn, too, the little bluish-black, plumlike fruits have ripened; standing singly or in twos or threes at the summit of each slender stalk. Though slightly acid and rather bitter, they seem to be relished by many birds and by bears, foxes, raccoons, opossums, and squirrels.

As a timber tree the black gum was once universally despised. But though the early settlers found that they couldn't even split it to make decent fence rails, they did find a use for the hollow trunks. These they sawed up into short lengths to be used as beehives, to which they usually gave the name of "bee gums." The light yellow to pale brownish-gray wood is moderately hard, strong, and stiff, and has a twisted, interlocking grain which is what makes it so tough and difficult to split. Today it is better appreciated and is used for furniture, gunstocks, and barrels. Cut into veneer, it goes into baskets, berry boxes, and egg crates.

The black gum's range extends from Maine westward through southern Ontario to Michigan, thence southwestward into eastern Texas. East of the Mississippi it is found southward into Florida and the Gulf coast.

*Nyssa* is the Greek name of a water nymph, and *sylvatica* means "of the woods." Locally the tree is called pepperidge, sourgum, or black tupelo.

## WATER TUPELO (*Nyssa aquatica*)

Like the bald cypress—which is almost always its companion—the water tupelo thrives with its feet in the water—hence its scientific name *aquatica* —and its trunk bulges conspicuously at the base like that of its companion. The water tupelo grows in deep coastal-plain swamps from southeastern Virginia south to northern Florida, west to southeastern Texas, and northward in the Mississippi Valley to southern Illinois and southeastern Missouri. A tree of more than moderate size, it commonly attains a height of 80 to 100 feet, with a trunk 3 to 4 feet in diameter above the greatly swollen base. A tree in the Wateree River swamp near Camden, South Carolina, is reported to have had a height of 110 feet, and a trunk circumference of 18 feet 1 inch at 4½ feet above the ground.

Among other trees that grow in its swampy domain, the water tupelo can be distinguished by its oval-shaped leaves, measuring from 5 inches to a foot long and commonly, though not always, having one or more big, wavy teeth on their margins. On the upper surface the leaves are a bright, shiny green; underneath they are paler and more or less softly hairy, and they are borne on stout leaf stalks from 1 to 3 inches in length. Between March and May two kinds of small greenish-white flowers appear on the branchlets. The male or stamen-bearing flowers form dense little clusters at the ends of long stalks. The female or pistil-bearing flowers are also stalked but solitary, and by September or October they have developed into dark-purplish, one-seeded, plumlike fruits about an inch in length.

The water tupelo is the principal source of commercial tupelo lumber, which is used mainly for furniture, broom handles, boxes, and crates. The wood of the swollen trunk bases and roots, which is spongy and much lighter than the rest, is used locally for bottle corks and fish-net floats. The flowers are an important source of honey that does not crystallize.

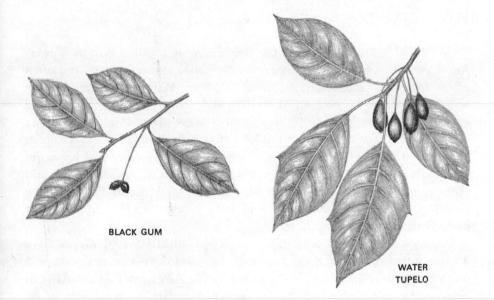

BLACK GUM

WATER
TUPELO

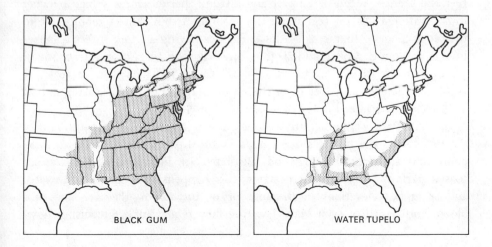

BLACK GUM

WATER TUPELO

# DOGWOOD FAMILY

## FLOWERING DOGWOOD (*Cornus florida*)

❧ FEW native North American trees are more admired than the flowering dogwood. It grows as an understory tree in hardwood forests, and often along fencerows and roadsides, from southern Maine westward through southern Ontario to southern Wisconsin and south to central Florida and eastern Texas. In addition, it has been widely planted in parks, along streets and highways, and about millions of our dwellings. Atlanta, Georgia, proclaims itself the "Dogwood City," and many other cities and towns, in the Southeast and elsewhere, likewise take pride in "dogwood trails" and other plantings of this attractive little native tree. Missouri has made the flowering dogwood its state teee, and both North Carolina and Virginia have chosen it as their state flower.

Usually a small tree rarely as much as 40 feet in height, with a trunk from 8 to 18 inches in diameter, the flowering dogwood does occasionally attain a much larger size. The champion reported by the American Forestry Association—a tree near Oriole in Somerset County, Maryland—has a height of 30 feet and branch spread of 42 feet and a trunk that measures 5 feet 4 inches in circumference at 4½ feet above the ground. Arthur Stupka reports one in the Great Smoky Mountains National Park as having a trunk 5 feet 4 inches in circumference. Coker and Totten, in *Trees of the Southeastern States,* report that one tree in northeastern North Carolina had a trunk 2 feet 2⅕ inches in diameter at 2 feet from the ground, and another measuring 1 foot 10⅕ inches in diameter at breast height.

In early spring, either shortly before the new leaves appear or just as they are unfolding, the button-shaped buds at the tips of the winter twigs expand into the familiar dogwood blossoms. In Florida and the warmer coastal parts of other Southern states, this happens in March. Northward, and at higher elevations in the interior of the South, the tree does not bloom until April or even May. The true flowers are small, greenish-yellow, and bunched in a dense little cluster or head in the center of what many suppose is the blossom. What appear to be petals with brown-edged notches at their tips are two pairs of modified leaves, or bracts, which are brilliant white or sometimes pink. Legend has it that the flowering dogwood furnished the wood for the cross on which Jesus died, and that forever after it had its slender, twisted shape, with flowers in the form of a cross and nail prints at their tips. It is a beautiful legend, though it fails to explain what this native American tree was doing in the Holy Land at the time of Christ.

In summer the flowering dogwood has pairs of oval-shaped, bright green leaves with a prominent midrib and five or six pairs of lateral veins, which curve so as to parallel the smooth leaf margin. At the approach of fall the leaves turn bright red. In fall, too, the little, egg-shaped, one-seeded, berry-like fruits which have developed from the spring flowers turn brilliant scarlet. They do not usually remain long for squirrels and many kinds of birds eat them, thereby rendering the dogwood the service of scattering its seeds.

The trunks of larger trees have an alligator-skin bark, dark reddish-brown to blackish and broken into small square or roundish blocks. The Indians boiled the bitter inner bark and used it for the treatment of fevers, and early settlers made a similar brew which they used as a cure for malaria. During the Civil War, while Southern ports were blockaded by the Union Navy, dogwood bark was used in the Confederate states as a substitute for quinine. From it the Indians also obtained a scarlet dye which they used to color feathers, blankets, and other objects.

The flowering dogwood's hard, tough, heavy, close-grained wood is preferred for the shuttles used in textile mills, because it stays smooth under constant wear. It also goes into spools and bobbins, butchers' skewers, golf-club heads, mallets, chisel handles, pulleys, and jewelers' blocks. The scientific name *Cornus,* derived from the Latin word for "horn," refers to the hardness of the wood, and *florida,* "flowering," refers to the showy petallike bracts.

## PACIFIC DOGWOOD (*Cornus nuttallii*)

This western relative of the eastern flowering dogwood is found in forests along the Pacific coast, from British Columbia southward in the mountains to southern California. On the western slope of the Sierra Nevada it occurs at elevations up to between 4,000 and 5,000 feet.

Usually this is a small or medium-sized tree, less than 60 feet in height, with a trunk between 1 and 2 feet in diameter. Occasionally it grows much larger. The present champion, according to the American Forestry Association, is a tree near Lowell in Clearwater County, Idaho. It has a height of 30 feet and the circumference of its trunk is 1 foot 9 inches at 4½ feet above the ground.

As compared with the flowering dogwood, this is a smooth-looking tree. The bark of the rather straight trunk is ashy-brown to reddish, and smooth; only on larger, older trunks does it become broken into very small, thin

**FLOWERING DOGWOOD**

**PACIFIC DOGWOOD**

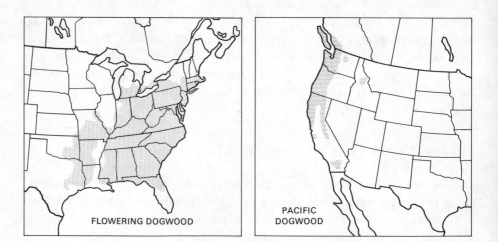

**FLOWERING DOGWOOD**

**PACIFIC DOGWOOD**

scales. It blooms rather late in the spring, when the leaves are relatively well developed, and not infrequently it blooms again in the fall. Although the flower heads of both species are similar, those of the Pacific dogwood are surrounded by from four to six large, petallike bracts which lack notches at their tips.

Aside from being the largest of the dogwoods, this is one of America's finest ornamental trees, and one deserving of extensive use along the Pacific coast, although unfortunately it cannot be grown with success in the eastern part of the country. John James Audubon, who first pictured it in his famous *Birds of America,* named the tree for Thomas Nuttall, who had collected a specimen on the Columbia River.

# HEATH FAMILY

## SOURWOOD (*Oxydendrum arboreum*)

❦ ALTHOUGH the sourwood is found from New Jersey west to southern Illinois, and south into northern Florida and southeastern Louisiana, it is most abundant in the southern Appalachian region. True, it often follows the streams all the way to or very near to the coast, and straggles northward across the Mason and Dixon Line as far as southwestern Pennsylvania, even making a few sorties across the broad Ohio River; but in these places it is not common and attracts little attention. Southward, in the Appalachians and their foothills, it seems to be everywhere, climbing the mountains to an elevation of between 4,500 and 5,000 feet.

Small and unimpressive in most places, the sourwood can make no claim whatsoever as a timber tree. Its wood is heavy and hard, and now and then a mountain farmer may use it for a tool handle; but that is about all. Occasionally a sourwood tree reaches a height of 40 to 60 feet, with a trunk a foot or a little more in diameter, but more often it does well if it is as much as 25 feet tall or has a trunk as much as 10 inches thick. The largest one on record grows—as might easily be guessed—in Great Smoky Mountains National Park. Its height is 80 feet, with a branch spread of about 40 feet and a trunk circumference of 7 feet 7 inches.

Long after the flowering dogwoods, the juneberries or sarvice trees, and the redbuds have had their time of glory—that is, from late June through the month of July—the sourwoods are covered with small, fragrant white blossoms. Like patches of a belated snow, they whiten the hillsides, and the bees have a busy time gathering their nectar. Individually the flowers are not very large—only about ⅓ inch long—and they are shaped like narrow urns. But in their profusion of one-sided, branched end clusters they make a splendid show. Each one is botanically perfect—that is, endowed with both stamens and a pistil—and eventually develops into a little, dry, five-angled capsule filled with tiny seeds.

After their flowers fade, the sourwoods return to comparative obscurity—

but not for long. Often before the middle of August the leaves begin to turn crimson, and as autumn progresses, the flaming foliage of this little tree accounts for much of the brilliant red seen in the southern Appalachian forests. The color often lasts throughout the month of October. In size and shape the leaves of a sourwood quite closely resemble those of the black cherry, but they are a much paler yellowish-green. Although they have no almondlike odor when bruised, they do have a distinctive sour taste, and hikers along the mountain trails often chew the leaves to allay thirst. The scientific name *Oxydendrum* comes from two Greek words meaning "sour" and "tree," and *arboreum* means "treelike"—most of its close relatives being merely shrubs.

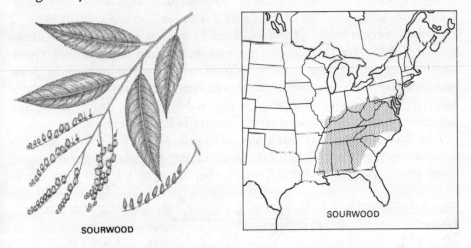

**SOURWOOD**

**SOURWOOD**

Sourwood honey is characteristically an Appalachian product, too, only rarely, if ever, reaching the shelves of city groceries. To obtain it one must take to the hills; but along almost any highway that traverses the sourwood country, home-made signs at many little rustic stands proclaim "Sourwood Honey for Sale." Those who like honey will find it a delight. Heavy-bodied and medium-light in color, it is slow to crystallize and has a distinctive tangy taste.

Some enterprising nurserymen offer the sourwood to the public as the Lily-of-the-Valley Tree, and indeed it makes a very attractive ornamental. The main trouble is that its requirements are rather exacting. Like its relatives the rhododendrons, the mountain laurel, and the blueberries, the sourwood needs an acid soil that is rich in humus, and it does not thrive on limestone soils. And in all the world it is the only sourwood—the sole known representative of the genus of the heath family to which it belongs.

## PACIFIC MADRONE (*Arbutus menziesii*)

On very poor sites the Pacific madrone may be only a shrub, but in some places it is a tree 80 to 125 feet tall, with a trunk from 2 to 4 feet in diameter. Thus it is the largest North American member of the heath family. The American Forestry Association's champion is a tree in Humboldt County, California, which has a height of 80 feet, a branch spread of 126 feet, and a trunk 30 feet 9 inches in circumference at 4½ feet above the ground.

Often known by its Spanish name of madroña, the tree grows from coastal British Columbia southward through western Washington and Oregon to California, where it occurs in the Coast Ranges and on the western slope of the Sierra Nevada below 4,000 feet. It grows in a variety of soils, but attains its best development on those that are well-drained and near sea level. Open-grown trees usually have a short, crooked, or leaning trunk, but in dense stands the trunk is generally straight and clean of branches for some distance above the ground. The wood is pale reddish-brown, heavy, dense, and fine-grained, but it is little used except in shuttles for textile mills.

The madrone is an evergreen tree, whose leaves persist on the branches until a new crop is fully grown. Oval-shaped, leathery in texture, dark, shiny green above and whitish beneath, they are 3 to 5 inches long, some-

PACIFIC
MADRONE

times toothed, and bluntly pointed. On the trunks of larger trees the thin reddish-brown bark is loosely scaly; on younger trunks and limbs it is smooth and red, peeling off in thin irregular flakes like the bark of a sycamore. The red-brown trunks, red branches, and shiny evergreen foliage distinguish it at once from all other trees within its range.

Between March and May, large showy clusters of small, white, urn-shaped flowers appear at the ends of the branchlets. They are followed in fall by bright orange-red, berrylike fruits which are often borne in great abundance, making the trees exceptionally beautiful at that time of the year. Although they have a dry custardy taste that is not very enjoyable, the fruits are eaten both raw and cooked by the Indians, and are an important food of the band-tailed pigeon and several other birds.

In 1814 the botanist Frederick Pursh named the tree *Arbutus menziesii* in honor of Archibald Menzies, a Scottish physician and naturalist who accompanied Captain Vancouver on his voyage of discovery in the Northwest. Although Menzies has the credit for being its discoverer, it was actually Padre Juan Crespi, who accompanied Caspar de Portola on the earliest overland trip northward through California, who first saw it, many years before. On November 5, 1769, he made a note in his diary of the "many madroños, though with smaller fruits than the Spanish." *Arbutus* is the classical Latin name of the tree to which Father Juan referred—the strawberry madrone of southern Europe.

**PACIFIC MADRONE**

# EBONY FAMILY

## COMMON PERSIMMON (*Diospyros virginiana*)

❧ IT is quite easy to tell a persimmon tree when its fruits are present; but many of the trees never produce fruits, since like those of the hollies, the stamen-bearing and pistil-bearing flowers are on separate trees. The greenish-yellow to milky-white flowers, shaped like little bells, appear on the young leafy shoots in May or June. All summer long, the trees are clad in shiny, dark-green leaves from 3 to about 6 inches in length, which are oval-shaped and smooth-edged, with rounded bases and pointed tips. In fall the leaves turn yellow, often with numerous blackish spots, and soon drop from the trees. The dark brown bark of the trunk is deeply broken up into small, squarish, scaly blocks, reminiscent of an alligator's hide.

Persimmons grow from southern Connecticut westward to central Illinois and southeastern Iowa, and southward to southern Florida and eastern Texas. Within this range they are found on a wide variety of soils, in forests and woodlots, along roadsides and fencerows, and in abandoned fields. In the southeastern United States—where it is most abundant—the persimmon will be found all the way from the coast to elevations of about 2,500 feet in the mountains.

As a rule it is a small or medium-sized tree, 30 to 50 feet in height, with a trunk usually less than a foot in diameter; but occasionally it attains a height of 130 feet, with a trunk diameter of as much as 5 feet. The American Forestry Association's champion—a tree near Johnson, Indiana—has a height of 80 feet, a branch spread of 73 feet 6 inches, and a trunk which measures 13 feet in circumference at 4½ feet above the ground.

Persimmon fruits are somewhat flattened, roundish berries which have the prominent woody remains of a calyx at their stem ends. Usually they are 1 inch to about 2 inches in diameter. At first they are orange-colored, often with red cheeks, but when fully ripe they become blackish-purple. Inside is the pulpy flesh, which becomes sweet when the fruits are fully ripe, and from one to eight large seeds. Individual trees vary greatly in the size and quality of the fruits they produce, as well as in their time of ripening. Some trees produce fine fruits which ripen by the latter part of August. Other trees produce fruits—good, bad, or indifferent—that do not ripen before October or November. Persimmons are eaten by many wild birds and mammals, and were important in the diet of the Southeastern Indians, who ate them fresh, or dried and ground them into a meal which they used for making bread.

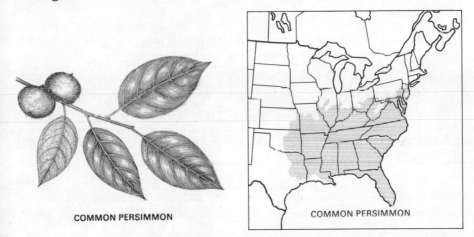

COMMON PERSIMMON

COMMON PERSIMMON

Hernando DeSoto and his conquistadors may well have been the first Europeans to taste the persimmon, as they wandered through the Southeastern wilderness just forty-eight years after the landing of Columbus. A narrative of their gold-seeking expedition records that the Indians offered them loaves made of the fruits, and that dried persimmons or "prunes" were found in many of the Indian villages that had been deserted before their arrival. Most likely, too, it was the Indians of Virginia who acquainted Captain John Smith with the persimmon. He learned something about it that a great many persons have discovered since, for he wrote, "If it be not ripe it will draw a man's mouth awrie with much torment."

Only a fully ripe persimmon is sweet and delicious; an unripe one is laden with astringent tannic acid. Ripe persimmons can be eaten raw or cooked, made into pudding, syrup, or even a kind of beer. Early settlers, and many Southerners during the Civil War, roasted the large seeds as a substitute for coffee. Quite recently it has been discovered that the leaves have an exceptionally high content of vitamin C, and that, either green or dried, they make a very acceptable tea.

The common persimmon is a member of the ebony family, and like its relatives it has a dense, hard, heavy wood in which the heartwood is dark brown to nearly black in color. The latter, which in fact, is sometimes called American ebony, is used extensively for rollers and the heads of golf clubs, while the lighter-colored sapwood is highly preferred for the shuttles used in textile mills.

The scientific name *Diospyros* comes from the Greek, and means "the grain of Jove"—a reference to the edible fruit—and *virginiana* means "of Virginia."

# OLIVE FAMILY

## The Ashes

❧    THE ash trees are members of the olive family, and there are about sixty-five species, growing chiefly in forests of the temperate regions of the Northern Hemisphere. Close to twenty species are found in North America. They can usually be distinguished from other trees by their compound leaves, which are arranged in pairs, or opposite each other, along the branchlets; although rarely—as in the singleleaf ash (*Fraxinus anomala*), found in the arid Southwest—the leaves are simple.

The flowers of most ashes appear early in the spring, before the leaves, and are not very showy. Those that bear stamens and those that bear pistils are usually found in clusters on separate trees, and the dusty pollen is carried by the wind. In a few species the flowers contain both stamens and pistils—and some of these, the so-called "flowering ashes," are showy, with four white petals. These flowers are often fragrant, too—a sign that they are pollinated by insects such as bees—and are borne in clusters at the ends of the leafy shoots. Only one American species has such showy flowers. This is the fragrant ash (*Fraxinus cuspidata*), a shrub or small tree found in the southwestern United States and Mexico.

The fruits of the ashes are quite unlike those of any other tree. At one end they have a long wing, shaped very much like a canoe paddle. A long and narrow chamber at the base contains a single seed. Borne in rather large and drooping clusters, the fruits are often quite conspicuous.

*Fraxinus* is the classical Latin name for an ash tree.

## WHITE ASH (*Fraxinus americana*)

The white ash is the largest and most abundant of its kind in North America, and it ranks high among the commercial hardwoods of the United

States. It becomes a big tree, commonly 70 to 80 feet in height, with a trunk 2 to 3 feet in diameter, sometimes attaining a height of 125 feet with a trunk diameter of 6 feet or more. The current champion listed by the American Forestry Association is a tree at Glenn Mills, Pennsylvania. It has a height of 80 feet, a branch spread of 82 feet, and a trunk measuring 22 feet 3 inches in circumference at 4½ feet above the ground.

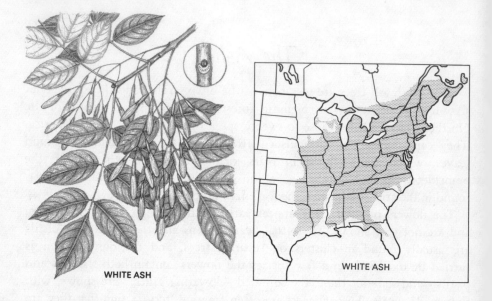

WHITE ASH

WHITE ASH

The white ash is found in forests from Nova Scotia westward through southern Quebec and Ontario to Minnesota, and southward to northern Florida and eastern Texas. It never forms pure stands, but occurs singly or in small groups in the company of other hardwoods or in a mixed forest of hardwoods and conifers; and seldom, if ever, is it even a dominant tree. Although it is found on a wide variety of soils, the white ash is most common where the soils are deep, fertile, and moist but well drained. In the Great Smoky Mountains National Park it grows to elevations of about 5,000 feet, but there the trees are small and stunted. The real giants are found in the rich, moist woodlands of lower altitudes.

It is not always easy to distinguish the white ash from its close relative the red ash. Both have two forms, with smooth or hairy leaves, and both have an ashy-gray bark with diamond-shaped fissures and narrow, forking ridges. The leaflets of the white ash are usually somewhat whitened on the lower surface, and its fruits have the wings attached only to the summit of the seed-bearing portion, whereas the wings of the red ash extend a little way down the sides. One of the best ways to distinguish the two is to look at the scars the fallen leaves have left on the twigs. In the white ash these scars have a a deep notch at the top that partly surrounds a bud. Those of the red ash are shallowly notched or nearly straight on the upper edge, and the bud stands above the leaf scar.

Baseball bats and hockey sticks, the frames of tennis rackets, polo mallets, swing seats, and oars—these are just a few of the familiar objects made from the heavy, hard, strong, tough wood of the white ash. To this list can be added shovel and hoe handles, furniture, butter tubs, baskets, boxes, and crates.

## RED ASH (*Fraxinus pennsylvanica*)

A typical red ash has velvety-downy twigs, and its leaves are divided into from seven to nine stalked leaflets, which are obscurely toothed on their edges and downy on the underside. In a variety called the green ash, both the twigs and the leaves are entirely smooth. This variety is usually more common and widespread than the velvety red ash, and it is much more important as a timber tree. Together the two forms have a wider range than any other species of American ash, a range that extends from Nova Scotia westward to central Saskatchewan and southward to northwestern Florida and central Texas.

Both varieties of the red ash are bottomland trees, commonly found along the banks of streams. Usually they are medium-sized, 30 to 60 feet in height

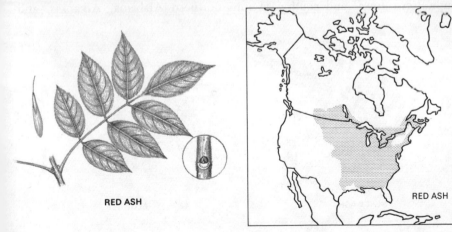

RED ASH

RED ASH

with a trunk 1 to 3 feet in diameter. But both occasionally grow much larger. The American Forestry Association's champion red ash, in Swan Pond Park, Riverside, Illinois, has a height of 99 feet and a trunk circumference of 10 feet 9 inches at 4½ feet above the ground. The champion green ash—a tree in Missouri's Big Oak Tree State Park—is 105 feet tall with a trunk circumference of 14 feet 8 inches.

Not only is the green ash the better timber tree, but it is the ash most often grown as a shade tree. It has been widely planted in the prairie region both as a shade tree and for shelterbelts. The wood is slightly heavier than that of the white ash, but does not quite equal it in quality, although as genuine white ash grows scarcer, the green ash supplies more and more of the lumberman's "white ash lumber."

The scientific name *pennsylvanica* means "of Pennsylvania."

## BLUE ASH (*Fraxinus quadrangulata*)

Those who despair of naming the species of ashes can expect an easier time with the blue ash. It is easily distinguished from all other American ashes by its four-angled and more or less four-winged twigs, indicated by the scientific name *quadrangulata*. Besides this outstanding feature, the bark also looks different. It is gray, but becomes divided into large scaly and shaggy plates. The inner bark contains a mucilaginous substance that turns blue upon exposure to the air, and which gave the tree its common name. From this bark the early settlers obtained a pigment which they used to dye cloth blue.

The blue ash is found from extreme southern Ontario southwestward to southeastern Iowa, and southward into northern Alabama, Arkansas, and

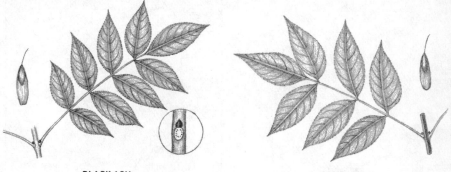

BLACK ASH                    BLUE ASH

northeastern Oklahoma. It is commonly a tree 50 to 80 feet in height with a trunk 1 to 3 feet in diameter, occasionally growing as high as 120 feet with a trunk diameter as much as 4 feet. The American Forestry Association reports a champion from Funk's Grove, Illinois—a tree 114 feet tall with a trunk measuring 10 feet 8 inches in circumference at 4½ feet above the ground. Although it sometimes grows in the bottomlands along with the white ash, the blue ash is more commonly found on dry limestone hills and uplands.

The blue ash is occasionally planted as a shade tree. The wood of the trees cut by lumbermen goes to market as "white ash lumber," but it is rather brittle and much inferior to genuine white ash.

## BLACK ASH (*Fraxinus nigra*)

Three features help to distinguish a black ash from its relatives. Its bark becomes broken into scales, which flake off when rubbed with the hand. Its leaves are divided into from seven to eleven stalkless leaflets, which have finely saw-toothed edges. And its gray twigs bear pointed, egg-shaped buds that are almost black, it is to these that the scientific name *nigra*, meaning "black," refers.

The black ash is essentially a northern tree, and is found from Newfoundland westward to southeastern Manitoba. It grows southward to Maryland, West Virginia, Indiana, Illinois, and Iowa. Because it occurs in swamps and bogs or along the banks of streams, it is often called the swamp ash.

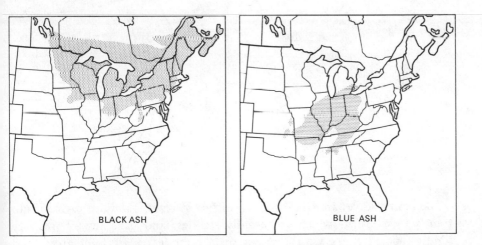

BLACK ASH

BLUE ASH

Commonly the black ash is a tree 40 to 50 feet in height with a trunk 1 to 2 feet in diameter, but occasionally it attains a height of 80 to 90 feet with a trunk diameter of 3 or 4 feet. The American Forestry Association's champion—a tree in Wayne County, Ohio—has a height of 108 feet and a trunk circumference of 9 feet 7 inches at 4½ feet above the ground. In the open the black ash develops a rounded, somewhat egg-shaped crown.

The wood of this ash is of medium weight, hardness, and strength. It is comparatively soft and rather coarse-grained. When pounded, the green wood breaks apart readily between the annual growth rings. Splints of black ash were widely used by the Indians for making pack baskets, whence it came to be called the basket ash. Still another name is hoop ash, a reminder of another frequent use made of splints from its wood. Black ash wood is still used for making baskets, and also for furniture, boxes, and crates.

## OREGON ASH (*Fraxinus latifolia*)

The Oregon ash is the only timber ash of the Pacific coast region. It is found in western Washington and Oregon, and in northern and central California. Commonly it is a tree 60 to 80 feet in height, with a trunk diameter of 2 to 3 feet, but under the most favorable conditions it sometimes attains a height of 120 feet, with a trunk diameter as great as 6 feet.

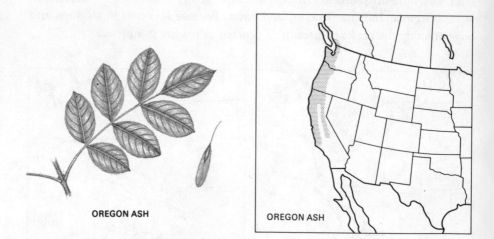

OREGON ASH

OREGON ASH

The paired leaves are from 5 to 14 inches in length, and are divided into from 5 to 7 leaflets which are usually stalkless and have smooth or very slightly toothed edges. On the upper surface the leaves are light green, and the lower surface is usually hairy but occasionally smooth. The fruits are from 1 to 2 inches long, with wings extending to or slightly below the middle of the seed portion. The trunk of the tree has a dark-gray or grayish-brown bark, with diamond-shaped fissures and forking ridges.

The wood of the Oregon ash is comparable to that of the eastern white ash, and it is used for furniture, tool handles, boxes, and crates; but as a timber tree the species is of only secondary importance.

The scientific name *latifolia* means "broad-leaved," and refers to the leaflets.

# BIGNONIA FAMILY

## NORTHERN CATALPA (*Catalpa speciosa*)

❧ CATALPAS are among the most familiar of trees, for they are widely planted for shade and ornamental purposes. Small boys know the catalpa as the "Indian toby," and fishermen as the "fish-bait" tree. Most people are familiar with its big, smooth-edged, heart-shaped leaves, and the large, showy clusters of white flowers which appear on the tree in spring. *Catalpa* is a Cherokee Indian name which the early settlers and also the botanists quickly adopted, although some people use the name catawba tree or Indian bean. *Speciosa* means "showy," and refers to the flowers.

The northern catalpa is the largest of two American species. Originally it occurred from southwestern Indiana west to Missouri and southward to western Tennessee and northeastern Arkansas. Today it is found far beyond

NORTHERN CATALPA

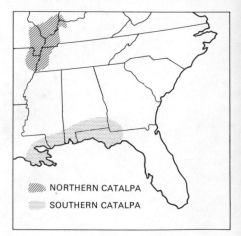

////// NORTHERN CATALPA

SOUTHERN CATALPA

that former range, and in many places it has escaped to grow as a wild tree. In the rich bottomlands of the Ohio basin, in southern Indiana and Illinois, it commonly attains its greatest size. There it may sometimes reach a height of 100 to 125 feet, with a trunk from 3 to 5 feet in diameter, although elsewhere it is usually somewhat smaller. The American Forestry Association's champion, however, is a tree at Lansing, Michigan, which has a height of 93 feet and a trunk 17 feet 4 inches in circumference at 4½ feet above ground.

The leaves of the catalpa are in opposite pairs, or sometimes in whorls of three, on the stout branchlets. They have rather long, stout, round stalks, and the heart-shaped blades of the northern catalpa are 8 inches to a foot long, 5 to 8 inches wide, and long-pointed at the tip. Between late May and early July the clusters of showy flowers appear; their white corollas are two-lipped and somewhat bell shaped, with five frilly margined lobes. Within the throat are two yellow stripes and some inconspicuous purplish-brown spots. The flowers are followed by slender, round, thick-walled pods from 10 to 20 inches long, filled with seeds which have two flattened wings with fringed tips. All winter they hang on the trees, and toward spring they split in two to liberate the seeds.

Catalpa wood is rather light, weak, and soft, but durable in contact with the soil. Thus the most important use made of it is for fence posts, though occasionally it is used for furniture, picture frames, handles, and other small items. The larvae of the catalpa sphinx, one of the hummingbirdlike moths, feed on the leaves, sometimes until the tree is completely defoliated. These caterpillars, with dark-green markings on their bodies and a sharp horn at the tail end, are much sought for fish bait, and fisherman know them as "catawba worms."

## SOUTHERN CATALPA (*Catalpa bignonioides*)

The other American species, the southern catalpa, is a somewhat smaller and less hardy but equally familiar tree. Originally it was found in the Gulf Coast region from southwestern Georgia and northwestern Florida to Louisiana; but it, too, has spread widely through cultivation. Its leaves are smaller and broader, and have an unpleasant odor when crushed. The flowers are borne in somewhat denser clusters, and are more thickly spotted with brownish-purple within; and the thin-walled pods are filled with seeds that have pointed rather than squarish tips.

The scientific name *bignonioides* means "bignonialike" and refers to a vine belonging to the same plant family as the catalpas.

# APPENDIX

## *Illustrated Glossary*

*alternate leaves.* Leaves that are spaced singly along a stem or twig.
*anther.* The part of a stamen in which the pollen is produced.
*awllike.* Shaped like an awl; small, stiff, and tapered to a sharp point.
*axil.* The upper angle formed by a leaf with the twig; also the similar angle formed
by one of the main veins of a leaf with the midrib.

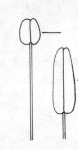

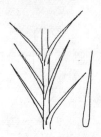

Alternate leaves          Anther          Awl-like          Axil

*bract.* A modified leaf or a scale at the base of a flower or of a flower cluster.

*bud.* An undeveloped stem or branch, flower, or flower cluster.

*calyx.* The outermost series of organs in a flower, which are often, but not always, green and leaflike.

*catkin.* A flower cluster, often drooping, which is made up of scales bearing either stamens or pistils but never both.

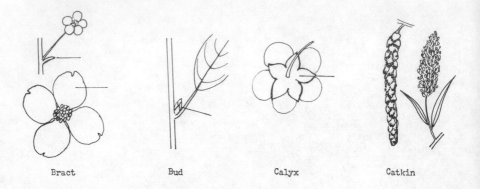

Bract             Bud             Calyx             Catkin

*compound leaf.* A leaf in which the blade is completely divided into smaller leaflike portions called *leaflets.* There is a bud in the axil of a leaf but buds are never present in the axils of the leaflets.

*corolla.* A term used for the petals of a flower, particularly when they are united into a cup or tube.

*double-toothed.* A leaf margin in which larger teeth in turn have smaller teeth on them.

*filament.* The stalklike part of a stamen which supports the anther.

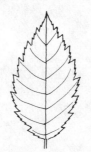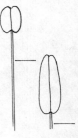

Compound leaf         Corolla         Double-toothed         Filament

*leaf scar.* A scar left on a twig by a fallen leaf.

*lenticel.* A small corky dot on a twig which marks an opening permitting the exchange of gasses with the atmosphere.

*lobed.* Having lobes or fingerlike projections, or deep indentations which often extend halfway or more to the midrib in the case of a leaf.

*midrib.* The central or main vein of a leaf.

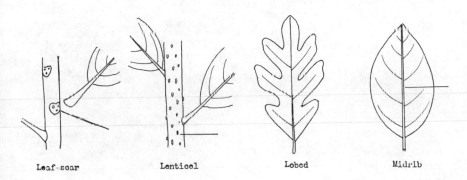

Leaf-scar                Lenticel                Lobed                Midrib

*opposite leaves.* Leaves which are placed in pairs, one directly across the stem from the other.

*ovary.* The basal part of a pistil inside of which are one or more *ovules* which, following fertilization, develop into seeds.

*petal.* A more or less leaflike, usually white or colored organ in a flower.

*pistil.* The organ of a flower that receives the pollen and produces the seed.

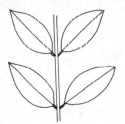 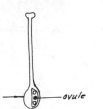  

Opposite leaves          Ovary                Petal                Pistil

*scalelike.* Small leaves resembling scales and usually overlapping one another like the shingles on a roof.

*sepal.* One of the outermost organs of a flower, often leaflike and green in color, which serve to protect other flower parts in the bud stage.

*simple leaf.* A leaf in which the flattened portion or blade is in one piece (see *compound leaf*).

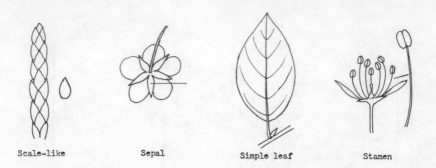

Scale-like          Sepal          Simple leaf          Stamen

*stamen.* An organ that produces the pollen.

*stigma.* The part of a pistil that receives the pollen.

*stipule.* A small scalelike or leaflike structure at the base of a leaf stalk, usually occurring in pairs.

*stomata.* Microscopic openings, mostly on the lower surfaces of leaves, which permit the exchange of gases with the atmosphere.

*style.* A stalklike portion of a pistil connecting the ovary and stigma.

Stigma          Stipule          Stomata          Style

# Identification Guide to Familiar Trees

1 ⎰
- a. If the tree has very large fan-shaped or featherlike leaves which are in a cluster at the top of the trunk, it is a . . . . . . . . . Palm
- b. If the tree has stiff bayonetlike leaves which are clustered on a few very stout branches, it is a . . . . . . . . . . . . . . . . . . . . Yucca
- c. If the tree has a columnlike stem (and often similar branches) with long grooves and ridges which are armed with spines, it is a . . . . . . . . . . . . . . . . . . . . . . . . . . . . . . . . . Cactus
- d. If the tree is ordinary in appearance, with a trunk and many branches, go to . . . . . . . . . . . . . . . . . . . . . . . . . Number 2

2 ⎰
- a. If the tree has needlelike leaves, awllike leaves, or small scalelike leaves, go to . . . . . . . . . . . . . . . . . . . . . . . . . . . . . Number 3
- b. If the tree has ordinary leaves with flattened blades, go to . . . . . . . . . . . . . . . . . . . . . . . . . . . . . . . . . . . . Number 16

3 ⎰
- a. If the leaves are needlelike, go to . . . . . . . . . . . . . . Number 4
- b. If the leaves are scalelike (or awllike on young growth), go to . . . . . . . . . . . . . . . . . . . . . . . . . . . . . . . . . . . . Number 12

4 ⎰
- a. If the needles are in bundles of two to five (rarely just one), with a sheath at the base, it is a . . . . . . . . . . . . . . . . . . . . . Pine
- b. If there are many needles in clusters on short spurs (except on the leading shoots), it is a . . . . . . . . . . . . . . . . . . . . . . . Larch
- c. If the needles are arranged singly along the twigs, without a sheath at the base, go to . . . . . . . . . . . . . . . . . . . . . . . . Number 5

5 ⎰
- a. If peglike bases of the needles remain on the twigs after the needles fall, making the twigs rough, go to . . . . . . . . . . . . . Number 6
- b. If the twigs are smooth or nearly so after the needles fall, go to . . . . . . . . . . . . . . . . . . . . . . . . . . . . . . . . . . . . Number 9

6 ⎰
- a. If the needles are soft and are blunt at the tip, it is a . Hemlock
- b. If the needles are stiff and are sharply pointed at the tip, go to . . . . . . . . . . . . . . . . . . . . . . . . . . . . . . . . . . . . Number 7

7 ⎰
- a. If the needles spread from all sides of the twigs and are usually four-sided, it is a . . . . . . . . . . . . . . . . . . . . . . . . . Spruce
- b. If the needles are in two rows and are flattened, go to Number 8

8
  a. If the needles are more than 1 inch long, have two white lines beneath, and have an unpleasant odor when bruised, it is a . . . . . . . . . . . . . . . . . . . . . . . . . . . . . . . . . . . . . . .Torreya
  b. If the needles are 1 inch or less long, do not have two white lines beneath, and are not unpleasantly scented when bruised, it is a . . . . . . . . . . . . . . . . . . . . . . . . . . . . . . . . . . . . . . .Yew

9
  a. If the needles are blunt, rounded, or notched at the tip, go to . . . . . . . . . . . . . . . . . . . . . . . . . . . . . . . . . . . .Number 10
  b. If the needles are pointed at the tip, go to . . . . . . .Number 11

10
  a. If the needles have short stalks and if the buds are cone-shaped, sharply pointed, and smooth, it is . . . . . . . . . . . . . .Douglas fir
  b. If the needles are stalkless and if the blunt-pointed or roundish buds are more or less crusted with white resin, it is a  Fir

11
  a. If the needles are soft and pale green beneath and both the needles and the slender branchlets which bear them are shed in the fall, it is a . . . . . . . . . . . . . . . . . . . . . . . . . . . . . . . . . . . . .Bald cypress
  b. If the needles are stiff and show two white lines beneath, and if both old and new needle-bearing branchlets are present, it is a. . . . . . . . . . . . . . . . . . . . . . . . . . . . . . . . . . . . . . . Redwood

12
  a. If all of the leaves are scalelike, overlapping like the shingles on a roof, go to . . . . . . . . . . . . . . . . . . . . . . . . . . . . . . .Number 13
  b. If both scalelike and some sharply pointed (awllike) leaves are present, go to . . . . . . . . . . . . . . . . . . . . . . . . . . . . .Number 15

13
  a. If the scalelike leaves are less than $\frac{1}{16}$ inch wide and the branchlets are but slightly flattened, it is a . . . . . . . . . . . . . . .White cedar
  b. If the scalelike leaves are more than $\frac{1}{16}$ inch wide and the branchlets look as if they had been pressed flat, go to Number 14

14
  a. If the leaves are in whorls of fours, it is an . . . . . . .Incense cedar
  b. If the leaves are in opposite pairs, it is an . . . . . . .Arborvitae

15
  a. If the leaves are single and spirally arranged, it is a  Giant sequoia
  b. If the leaves are opposite or in whorls of three's, the branchlets are rounded or four-sided, and the cones are berrylike, it is a . . . . . . . . . . . . . . . . . . . . . . . . . . . . . . . . . . . . . . .Juniper
  c. If the leaves are opposite in pairs, the branchlets are slightly flattened, and the tree has small woody cones, it is a White cedar

16
  a. If the leaves are arranged opposite one another on the twigs like this Y or sometimes in whorls of threes, go to . .Number 17
  b. If the leaves are placed alternately along the twigs, like this, Y go to . . . . . . . . . . . . . . . . . . . . . . . . . . . . . . . . . . . .Number 20

17
a. If the leaves are compound, with several leaflets on a single stem (you can tell a leaflet from a leaf because there is no bud at its base), go to .............................. Number 18
b. If the leaves are simple (not divided into leaflets), go to....................................... Number 19

18
a. If five or more leaflets are spread fingerlike at the summit of the leaf stalk, it is a ............................. Buckeye
b. If the three to five leaflets each have a few large and coarse teeth, it is a ..................................... Maple (Box elder)
c. If the leaflets are untoothed or finely or inconspicuously toothed, and are arranged along an extension of the leaf stalk, it is an ..................................,,............... Ash

19
a. If the leaves are often in threes, heart-shaped, and smooth on the edge, it is a ....................... Catalpa
b. If the leaves are always in pairs and smooth-edged, and the veins are curved so that they tend to parallel the leaf margin, it is a ..................................... Dogwood
c. If the leaves are always in pairs, three- or five-lobed, and also often toothed, it is a ........................... Maple

20
a. If the leaves are compound, with several leaflets along a common stem (you can tell a leaflet from a leaf because there is no bud at its base), go to ........................... Number 21
b. If the leaves are simple (not divided into leaflets), go to ..................................... Number 27

21
a. If the leaflets are toothed like a saw and they are fragrant when they are crushed, go to ...................... Number 22
b. If the leaflets have smooth edges (or have a few very inconspicuous teeth) and are not fragrant when they are crushed, go to ................................. Number 23

22
a. If the leaves have from eleven to twenty-three leaflets and the pith in the twigs shows plates like this ▤ when cut lengthwise, it is a ,................................... Walnut
b. If the leaves have from five to seventeen leaflets and the pith in the twigs appears solid when cut lengthwise, it is a ... Hickory or Pecan

23
a. If the leaflets are rounded or blunt at the tip, go to . Number 24
b. If the leaflets are pointed at the tip, go to ....... Number 26

24
a. If all or some of the leaves are twice compound (divided into stems which in turn have leaflets), go to ............. Number 25
b. If all of the leaves are once compound, with from seven to nineteen

leaflets, and the twigs have pairs of short spines where the leaves are attached, it is a . . . . . . . . . . . . . . . . . . . . . . . . . Locust

25 —
a. If the leaves are about 1 inch long with two or three pairs of leaflets on each of their two branches, and the twigs have short spines, it is a . . . . . . . . . . . . . . . . . . . . . . . . . . Paloverde
b. If the leaves are 6 to 12 inches long with numerous leaflets, and only some of the leaves are twice compound, or if large and branched thorns are present, it is a . . . . . . . . . . . . . Honey locust

26 —
a. If the leaves are twice compound (divided into stems which in turn have leaflets) and the twigs are very stout, it is a . . . Kentucky coffee tree
b. If the leaves are once compound, with from three to seven firm leaflets, and the tree has red fruits splitting into three parts, it is a . . . . . . . . . . . . . . . . . . . . . . . . . . . . . . . . . . . . . Gumbo limbo

27 —
a. If the leaves have lobes or both teeth and lobes, go to Number 28
b. If the leaves have no lobes but the edges are toothed, go to . . . . . . . . . . . . . . . . . . . . . . . . . . . . . . . . . . . . Number 31
c. If the edges of the leaves are smooth, with neither teeth nor lobes, go to . . . . . . . . . . . . . . . . . . . . . . . . . . . . . . . . . . . Number 43

28 —
a. If the leaves have a pronounced fragrance when crushed, go to . . . . . . . . . . . . . . . . . . . . . . . . . . . . . . . . . . . . . Number 29
b. If the leaves are not noticeably fragrant when crushed, go to . . . . . . . . . . . . . . . . . . . . . . . . . . . . . . . . . . . Number 30

29 —
a. If the leaves, or at least some of them, have two or three lobes and the twigs are green, it is . . . . . . . . . . . . . . . . . . . . . Sassafras
b. If the leaves are star-shaped and also have saw-toothed edges, it is a . . . . . . . . . . . . . . . . . . . . . . . . . . . . . . . . . . . Sweet gum
c. If the leaves are broadly V-shaped at the top and have four to six lobes, and the twigs have a narrow ring where each leaf is attached, it is a . . . . . . . . . . . . . . . . . . . . . . . . . . . . . . . . . . Tulip tree

30 —
a. If the leaves have several main veins branching from the summit of the leaf stalk, and the swollen base of the leaf stalk covers a bud, it is a . . . . . . . . . . . . . . . . . . . . . . . . . . . . . . . . . Sycamore
b. If the leaves have but one main vein (the midrib) with smaller side branches, and the leaves tend to be grouped close together at the tips of the twigs, it is an . . . . . . . . . . . . . . . . . . . . . . Oak

31 —
a. If the leaves have wavy edges with a few large and spiny teeth, it is an . . . . . . . . . . . . . . . . . . . . . . . . . . . . . . . . . American holly
b. If the leaves are coarsely toothed with but one tooth to each straight side vein, go to . . . . . . . . . . . . . . . . . . . . . . . . . . . . Number 32
c. If the edges of the leaves are saw-toothed with more than one tooth to each side vein, go to . . . . . . . . . . . . . . . . . Number 35

32
- a. If the leaves tend to be grouped close together at the tips of the twigs, and if the fruit is an acorn, go to . . . . . . . . Number 33
- b. If the leaves are all well spaced along the twigs, and the fruits are not acorns, go to . . . . . . . . . . . . . . . . . . . . . . . . . . Number 34

33
- a. If the leaves are evergreen, thick, leathery, and downy or bluish-white beneath, and if the acorn cup is burlike, it is a Tanoak
- b. If the leaves are not evergreen and the acorn cups are not burlike, it is an . . . . . . . . . . . . . . . . . . . . . . . . . . . . . . . . Oak

34
- a. If the leaves are about twice as long as wide and the buds are very long, slender, and sharply pointed, it is an . . . . . . . American beech
- b. If the leaves are 3 or more times as long as wide and the buds are shaped somewhat like a grain of wheat, it is a . . . . Chestnut

35
- a. If the leaf is long and narrow (4 or more times as long as wide), go to . . . . . . . . . . . . . . . . . . . . . . . . . . . . . . . . . . Number 36
- b. If the leaf is oval or egg-shaped, go to . . . . . . . . . Number 38
- c. If the leaf is heart-shaped or triangular, go to . . . . . Number 42

36
- a. If the leaves have prominent broad stipules (like a pair of tiny leaves at the base of the leaf stalks) and the buds are covered with a single scale, it is a . . . . . . . . . . . . . . . . . . . . . . . . . Willow
- b. If the leaves have but narrow stipules or no stipules and the buds have more than one scale, go to . . . . . . . . . . . . . . . Number 37

37
- a. If the leaves have a bitter cherrylike odor when they are bruised, it is a . . . . . . . . . . . . . . . . . . . . . . . . . . . . . . . . . Black cherry
- b. If the leaves lack such an odor but they have a sour taste when they are chewed, it is a . . . . . . . . . . . . . . . . . . . . . . . . . Sourwood

38
- a. If the veins of the leaves are straight and evenly spaced, and the leaf edges have uneven teeth of two sizes, go to . . . Number 39
- b. If the veins of the leaves are not straight and evenly spaced, and the leaf edges have more or less even and uniform teeth, go to . . . . . . . . . . . . . . . . . . . . . . . . . . . . . . . . . . : Number 41

39
- a. If the leaves are lopsided or uneven at the base, it is an . . . . . . . . . . . . . . . . . . . . . . . . . . . . . . . . . . . . . . .Elm
- b. If the leaves are quite even or symmetrical at the base, go to . . . . . . . . . . . . . . . . . . . . . . . . . . . . . . . . . . . . Number 40

40
- a. If some of the leaves are in pairs on short spurs, it is a . . . . . . . . . . . . . . . . . . . . . . . . . . . . . . . . . . . . . Birch
- b. If none of the leaves are paired on spurs and if small woody "cones" are present, it is an . . . . . . . . . . . . . . . . . . Alder

- a. If the leaves have three main veins arising from a lopsided base and they are rough on the upper surface, it is a . . . Hackberry

41 ‒ b. If the leaves are symmetrical at the base and smooth and shiny above and are somewhat fragrant when bruised, it is a . . . . . . . . . . . . . . . . . . . . . . . . . . . . . . . . . . . . . Poplar

42 ‒
a. If the leaves are lopsided or slanted at the base and the leaf stalks are rounded, it is a . . . . . . . . . . . . . . . . . . . . . . . . . Basswood
b. If the leaves are symmetrical at the base and the leaf stalks are flattened as if they had been pinched in from the sides, it is a . . . . . . . . . . . . . . . . . . . . . . . . . . . . . . . . . . . Cottonwood or Aspen
c. If the leaves are paired on short spurs, it is a . . . . . Birch

43 ‒
a. If the leaves are heart-shaped, it is a . . . . . . . . . . . . Redbud
b. If the leaves are not heart-shaped, go to . . . . . . . . Number 44

44 ‒
a. If either the bruised leaves or broken twigs have a pleasant aromatic odor, go to . . . . . . . . . . . . . . . . . . . . . . . . . . . . . . . Number.45
b. If neither the leaves or twigs have a noticeable odor, go to . . . . . . . . . . . . . . . . . . . . . . . . . . . . . . . . . . . . Number 47

45 ‒
a. If the twigs are encircled by a narrow ring where each leaf is attached, it is a . . . . . . . . . . . . . . . . . . . . . . . . . . . . Magnolia
b. If the twigs are not encircled by such narrow rings, go to . . . . . . . . . . . . . . . . . . . . . . . . . . . . . . . . . . . . Number 46

46 ‒
a. If the leaves have a prominent network of small veins on the underside and if the twigs are green, it is a . . . . . . . . . . . California laurel
b. If the leaves do not have conspicuous small veins beneath and if the twigs are brownish, it is a . . . . . . . . . . . . . . . . . . Red bay

47 ‒
a. If the leaves have three main veins arising from a lopsided base, it is a . . . . . . . . . . . . . . . . . . . . . . . . . . . . . . . . . . . Hackberry
b. If the leaves have but one main vein (a midrib) and the leaf bases are symmetrical, go to . . . . . . . . . . . . . . . . . . . . . . . Number 48

48 ‒
a. If the leaves tend to be grouped close together at the tips of the twigs and if the fruit is an acorn, it is an . . . . . . . Oak
b. If the leaves are all well spaced along the twigs and if the fruit is not an acorn, go to . . . . . . . . . . . . . . . . . . . . . . . . . Number 49

49 ‒
a. If the leaves are evergreen (both old and new leaves present) and they are thick and leathery in texture, go to . . . . . . . Number 50
b. If the leaves are not evergreen and they are not particularly thick and leathery, go to . . . . . . . . . . . . . . . . . . . . . . . . Number 51

50 ‒
a. If a drop of milky sap appears when a leaf is pulled off the twig and if the twigs have a narrow ring where each leaf is attached, it is a . . . . . . . . . . . . . . . . . . . . . . . . . . . . . . . . . . . Strangler fig
b. If the twigs are not ringed and are reddish and the leaves have prominent veins on the underside, it is a . . . . . . . . . Pacific madrone

51
a. If the leaves are over 5 inches long and they occasionally have one to a few very large wavy teeth, it is a . . . . . . . . . . Water tupelo
b. If the leaves are less than 5 inches long and are never toothed, go to . . . . . . . . . . . . . . . . . . . . . . . . . . . . . . . . . . . Number 52

52
a. If the leaves are always pointed at the base and an end bud is present on the twig, it is a . . . . . . . . . . . . . . . . . . Black gum
b. If the leaves are mostly rounded at the base and no end bud is present on the twig, it is a . . . . . . . . . . . . . . . . . . Persimmon

# Champion Trees*

| Species | Circumference at 4½ feet | Height, in feet | Spread, in feet | Location |
|---|---|---|---|---|
| Alder, Red | 13' 9" | 92 | 54 | Polk County, Oregon |
| Ash, Black | 9' 7" | 108 | 48 | Wayne County, Ohio |
| Ash, Blue | 10' 8" | 114 | 54 | Funk's Grove, Illinois |
| Ash, Green | 14' 8" | 105 | 79 | Big Oak Tree State Park, Missouri |
| Ash, Oregon | 18' | | | Near Burlington, Oregon |
| Ash, White | 22' 3" | 80 | 82 | Glenn Mills, Pennsylvania |
| Aspen, Bigtooth | 17' 2" | 95 | 82 | Walker, New York |
| Aspen, Quaking | 11' 6" | 70 | 45 | Santa Fe National Forest, New Mexico |
| Basswood, American | 17' 1" | 103 | 103 | Queenstown, Maryland |
| Basswood, White | 13' 9" | 80 | 61 | Little Switzerland, North Carolina |
| Beech, American | 18' 5" | 91 | 96 | Saugatuck, Michigan |
| Birch, Black | 15' 2" | 70 | 87 | Near New Boston, New Hampshire |
| Birch, Gray | 7' 3" | 60 | 51 | Near Clarksville, Maryland |
| Birch, Paper | 10'11" | 96 | 93 | Lake Leelanau, Michigan |
| Birch, Red | 12' 4" | 98 | 72 | Near Odenton, Maryland |
| Birch, Yellow | 14' 1" | 90 | 64 | Great Smoky Mountains National Park, Tennessee |
| Buckeye, Ohio | 9' 9" | 85 | 40 | Champaign County, Ohio |
| Buckeye, Yellow | 15'11" | 85 | 54 | Great Smoky Mountains National Park, Tennessee |
| Butternut | 11' 9" | 85 | 92 | St. Joseph County, Michigan |
| Catalpa, Northern | 17' 4" | 93 | 74 | Lansing, Michigan |
| Catalpa, Southern | 15' 4" | 54 | 58 | Sparta, Michigan |
| Cedar, Alaska | 25' 6" | 134 | 25 | Mount Rainier National Park, Washington |
| Cedar, Atlantic White | 15' 6" | 87 | | Near Brewton, Alabama |
| Cedar, Eastern Red | 12' 2" | 76 | 45 | Near Roganville, Texas |

\* A.F.A. Champion Trees from list in May, 1966, issue of *American Forest*.

| Species | Circumference at 4½ feet | Height in feet | Spread in feet | Location |
|---|---|---|---|---|
| Cedar, Incense | 36' | | | Rouge River National Forest, California |
| Cedar, Northern White | 17' 2" | 111 | 38 | South Manitou Island, Michigan |
| Cedar, Port Orford | 27' 2" | 200 | | Coos County, Oregon |
| Cedar, Western Red | 66' 1" | 130 | 55 | Olympic National Park, Oregon |
| Cherry, Black | 23' 4" | 102 | 89 | Van Buren County, Michigan |
| Chestnut, American | 15' 8" | 90 | 64 | Oregon City, Oregon (planted) |
| Coffee Tree, Kentucky | 13' 7" | 84 | 60 | Near Hartford, Kentucky |
| Cottonwood, Black | 32' 6" | 101 | 60 | Near Haines, Alaska |
| Cottonwood, Eastern | 25' 9" | 131 | 129 | Wayne, Michigan |
| Cottonwood, Narrowleaved | 6' | 55 | 25 | Harney County, Oregon |
| Cucumber Tree | 18' 4" | 125 | 60 | Great Smoky Mountains National Park, Tennessee |
| Cypress, Bald | 39' 8" | 122 | 47 | Near Sharon, Tennessee |
| Cypress, Pond | 3' 1" | 56 | 9 | Near Newark, Ohio (planted) |
| Dogwood, Flowering | 5' 4" | 30 | 42 | Near Oriole, Maryland |
| Dogwood, Pacific | 1' 9" | 30 | | Near Lowell, Idaho |
| Elm, American | 24' 7" | 160 | 147 | Near Trigonia, Tennessee |
| Elm, Slippery | 21' 2" | 116 | 101 | Henderson, Kentucky |
| Fig, Florida Strangler | 22' 1" | 51 | 58 | Miami, Florida |
| Fir, Balsam | 7' | 116 | 33 | Porcupine Mountains State Park, Michigan |
| Fir, Douglas | 45' 5" | 221 | 61 | Olympic National Park, Washington |
| Fir, Fraser | 7' 9" | | | Great Smoky Mountains National Park, Tennessee |
| Fir, Grand | 22' 4" | 175 | 40 | Mount Rainier National Park, Washington |
| Fir, White | 27' 8" | 179 | 34 | Meridian, California |
| Gum, Black | 15' 9" | 130 | 100 | Near Urania, Louisiana |
| Gum, Sweet | 17'10" | 118 | 81 | New Madrid, Missouri |
| Gumbo Limbo | 5' 1" | 51 | 35 | Everglades National Park, Florida |
| Hackberry | 18' | 113 | 79 | Near Wayland, Michigan |
| Hemlock, Eastern | 19' 9" | 98 | 69 | Great Smoky Mountains National Park, Tennessee |
| Hemlock, Western | 27' 2" | 125 | 47 | Olympic National Park, Washington |
| Hickory, Bitternut | 12' 6" | 97 | 68 | Baltimore County, Maryland |

| Species | Circumference at 4½ feet | Height in feet | Spread in feet | Location |
|---|---|---|---|---|
| Hickory, Mockernut | 9' 2" | 112 | 58 | Sandy Spring, Maryland |
| Hickory, Pignut | 11' 5" | 165 | 60 | Baton Rouge, Louisiana |
| Hickory, Shagbark | 11' 5" | 100 | 113 | Chevy Chase, Maryland |
| Holly, American | 13' 4" | 53 | 61 | Near Hardin, Texas |
| Joshua Tree | 12' 6" | 32 | 37 | Joshua Tree National Monument, California |
| Larch, Western | 24' | 120 | 37 | Near Kootenai National Forest, Montana |
| Laurel, California | 36' 9" | | | Near Eleanor, California |
| Locust, Black | 15'11" | 85 | 60 | Near Jefferson, Indiana |
| Locust, Honey | 18' 9" | 92 | 112 | Queenstown, Maryland |
| Madrone, Pacific | 30' 9" | 80 | 126 | Humboldt County, California |
| Magnolia, Southern | 18' | 99 | 71 | Baton Rouge, Louisiana |
| Maple, Ash-Leaved | 13' 6" | 81 | 108 | Detroit, Michigan |
| Maple, Bigleaf | 23' 6" | 96 | 100 | Near Portland, Oregon |
| Maple, Red | 15' 4" | 136 | 95 | Near Utica, Michigan |
| Maple, Silver | 22'10" | 90 | 110 | Fryeburg-Harbor, Maine |
| Maple, Sugar | 19' 9" | 116 | 75 | Garrett County, Maryland |
| Oak, Black | 22' 3" | 125 | 85 | Warrensville Heights, Ohio |
| Oak, Bur | 20' 9" | 122 | 107 | Algonac, Michigan |
| Oak, California White | 27' 9" | 125 | | Near Middletown, California |
| Oak, Chestnut | 22' 3" | 95 | 108 | Easton, Maryland |
| Oak, Live | 35' | 78 | 168 | Near Hahnville, Louisiana |
| Oak, Pin | 16' | 135 | 135 | Saint Davids, Pennsylvania |
| Oak, Northern Red | 26' 4" | 78 | 104 | Ashford, Connecticut |
| Oak, Oregon White | 25' 6" | 120 | | Mendocino National Forest, California |
| Oak, Southern Red | 24' 1" | 122 | 132 | Cumberstone, Maryland |
| Oak, Scarlet | 15' 9" | 102 | 110 | Swarthmore, Pennsylvania |
| Oak, Water | 20' 3" | 77 | 100 | Near Center, Texas |
| Oak, White | 27' 8" | 95 | 165 | Wye Mills, Maryland |
| Oak, Willow | 21' 2" | 118 | 106 | Queenstown, Maryland |
| Palm, Royal | 4' 9" | 100 | 12 | Collier Seminole State Park, Florida |
| Palmetto, Cabbage | 3' 9" | 90 | 12 | Highlands Hammock State Park, Florida |
| Pecan | 21' 4" | 135 | 145 | Assumption Parish, Louisiana |
| Persimmon, Common | 13' | 80 | 74 | Near Johnson, Indiana |

| Species | Circumference at 4½ feet | Height in feet | Spread in feet | Location |
|---|---|---|---|---|
| Pine, Loblolly | 16′ 6″ | 128 | 64 | Near Ammon, Virginia |
| Pine, Lodgepole | 19′ 8″ | 110 | 37 | San Bernardino National Forest, California |
| Pine, Longleaf | 10′ 9″ | 113 | 40 | Autauga County, Alabama |
| Pine, Pinyon | 11′ 3″ | 33 | 44 | La Sal National Forest, Utah |
| Pine, Pitch | 8′ 3″ | 97 | 36 | Mays Landing, New Jersey |
| Pine, Ponderosa | 27′ 1″ | 162 | | Near Lapine, Oregon |
| Pine, Red | 8′10″ | 125 | 33 | Brule River State Forest, Wisconsin |
| Pine, Shortleaf | 10′ 7″ | 146 | 60 | Morganton, North Carolina |
| Pine, Slash | 10′ 5″ | 119 | 41 | Apalachicola National Forest, Florida |
| Pine, Sugar | 31′ 2″ | 170 | 56 | Stanislaus National Forest, California |
| Pine, Eastern White | 17′11″ | 151 | 48 | Brule River State Forest, Wisconsin |
| Pine, Western White | 21′ 3″ | 219 | 36 | Near Elk River, Idaho |
| Poplar, Balsam | 11′11″ | 89 | 78 | Cornell, Michigan |
| Red Bay | 8′ 6″ | 53 | 50 | Near Conroe, Texas |
| Redbud, Eastern | 8′ 3″ | | 46 | Dayton, Ohio |
| Redwood | 44′ | 368 | | Humboldt County, California |
| Sassafras | 16′ | 88 | 68 | Owensboro, Kentucky |
| Sequoia, Giant | 83′11″ | 272 | 90 | Sequoia National Park, California |
| Sourwood | 7′ 7″ | 80 | 40 | Great Smoky Mountains National Park, Tennessee |
| Spruce, Black | 11′ 9″ | 75 | 18 | Superior National Forest, Minnesota |
| Spruce, Blue | 15′ 8″ | 126 | 36 | Gunnison National Forest, Colorado |
| Spruce, Engelmann | 20′ 7″ | 140 | 34 | Williamette National Forest, Oregon |
| Spruce, Red | 13′10″ | 106 | 45 | Great Smoky Mountains National Park, North Carolina |
| Spruce, Sitka | 41′ 8″ | 214 | 50 | Olympic National Park, Washington |
| Spruce, White | 10′ 6″ | 116 | 27 | Superior National Forest, Minnesota |
| Sycamore, American | 32′10″ | 80 | 102 | Near South Bloomfield, Ohio |
| Tamarack | 11′ 5″ | 60 | 60 | Chaplin, Connecticut |
| Tanoak | 24′ 1″ | 80 | 84 | Near Cazedero, California |
| Torreya, California | 14′10″ | 141 | 39 | Near Mendocino, California |
| Tulip Tree | 24′ 3″ | 110 | 119 | Amelia, Virginia |
| Tupelo, Water | 4′ 10″ | 54 | 24 | Dunklin County, Missouri |
| Walnut, Black | 20′ 3″ | 108 | 128 | Anne Arundel County, Maryland |
| Willow, Black | 26′ 1″ | 85 | 79 | Traverse City, Michigan |
| Yew, Pacific | 14′ 8″ | 60 | 57 | Near Mineral, Washington |

# SUGGESTED READING

*The Book of Trees,* by William C. Grimm. 493 pp., illus., with keys for both summer and winter identification of the native and more common introduced trees of eastern North America exclusive of Florida. The Stackpole Company, Harrisburg, Pa., 1965.

*The Forest,* by Peter Farb. 192 pp., illus. Time, Inc., New York, 1963.

*Forest Trees of the Pacific Coast,* by Willard Ayres Eliot. 565 pp., illus. G. P. Putnam's Sons, New York, 1948.

*The Great American Forest,* by Rutherford Platt. 271 pp., illus. Prentice-Hall, Inc., Englewood Cliffs, N. J., 1965.

*Guide to Southern Trees,* by Elwood S. Harrar and J. George Harrar. 709 pp., illus., keys for identification of native trees of the southeastern states and Florida. Dover Publications, Inc., New York, 1962.

*Illustrated Guide to Trees and Shrubs: A Handbook of the Woody Plants of the Northeastern United States and Adjacent Regions,* by Arthur Harmount Graves. 271 pp., illus., with keys. Harper & Bros., New York, 1956.

*An Illustrated Manual of Pacific Coast Trees,* by Howard E. McMinn and Evelyn Maino. 409 pp., illus. University of California Press, Berkeley, 1956.

*Knowing Your Trees,* by G. H. Collingwood and Warren D. Brush; revised by Devereux Butcher. 349 pp., photographic illus., maps, covering 170 of the most common trees of the United States. American Forestry Association, Washington, D.C., 1964.

*The Living Forest,* by Jack McCormick. 127 pp., illus. Harper & Bros., New York, 1959.

*The National Forests,* by Arthur H. Carhart. 288 pp. Alfred A. Knopf, Inc., New York, 1959.

*A Natural History of Trees of Eastern and Central North America,* by Donald Culross Peattie. 606 pp., illus. Houghton Mifflin Co., Boston, Mass., 1950.

*A Natural History of Western Trees,* by Donald Culross Peattie. 751 pp., illus. Houghton Mifflin Co., Boston, Mass., 1953.

*The Native Trees of Florida,* by Erdman West and Lillian E. Arnold. 212 pp., illus., with key. University of Florida Press, Gainesville, 1952.

*Native Trees of Southern California,* by P. Victor Peterson. 136 pp., illus., maps. University of California Press, Berkeley, 1966.

*North American Trees,* by Richard J. Preston, Jr. 395 pp., illus., maps, keys to trees except those of Mexico and tropical United States. Iowa State University Press, Ames, 1961.

*1001 Questions Answered About Trees,* by Rutherford Platt. 318 pp., illus. Dodd, Mead & Co., New York, 1959.

*Pocket Guide to Alaska Trees,* by Raymond F. Taylor and Elbert L. Little, Jr. 63 pp., illus. U.S. Department of Agriculture Handbook 5, Government Printing Office, Washington, D.C., 1950.

*Rocky Mountain Trees,* by Richard J. Preston, Jr. 285 pp., illus. Iowa State University Press, Ames, 1947.

*Southwestern Trees: A Guide to the Native Species of New Mexico and Arizona,* by Elbert L. Little, Jr. 109 pp., illus. U.S. Department of Agriculture, Agriculture Handbook 9, Government Printing Office, Washington, D.C., 1950.

*This Green World,* by Rutherford Platt. 219 pp., illus. Dodd, Mead & Co., New York, 1952.

*The Tree Identification Book,* by George W. D. Symonds. 272 pp., photographic illus. covering 130 species of trees. M. Barrows & Co., New York, 1958.

*Trees and Shrubs of the Southwestern Deserts,* by Lyman D. Benson and Robert A. Darrow. 437 pp., illus. University of Arizona Press, Tucson, 1954.

*Trees and Shrubs of the Upper Midwest,* by Carl Otto Rosendahl. 411 pp., illus. University of Minnesota Press, Minneapolis, 1955.

*Trees of the Southeastern States,* by William C. Coker and Henry R. Totten. 419 pp., illus., with keys to trees of the Southeast except those of tropical Florida. University of North Carolina Press, Chapel Hill, 1945.

*Trees, Shrubs, and Woody Vines of the Great Smoky Mountains National Park,* by Arthur Stupka. 186 pp., some photographs, keys. University of Tennessee Press, Knoxville, 1964.

*Trees, Shrubs, and Woody Vines of the Southwest,* by Robert A. Vines. 1104 pp., illus., keys. University of Texas Press, Austin, 1960.

*Trees and Trails,* by Clarence J. Hylander. 237 pp., illus. Macmillan Co., New York, 1952.

*Trees: The Yearbook of Agriculture for 1949.* United States Department of Agriculture. 944 pp., illus. Government Printing Office, Washington, D.C.

*Western Forest Trees,* by James Berthold Berry. 212 pp., illus. Dover Publications, Inc., New York, 1964.

# INDEX

233

## DATE DUE

| | | |
|---|---|---|
| Mar 22 6 8 | 'AY 1 2 1982 | |
| Sep 14 6 8 | 'AY 2 6 1982 | |
| Oct 12 6 8 | AUG 4 1982 | |
| Sep 22 9 | JAN 2 0 1983 | |
| APR 18 '70 | Feb 21 1983 | |
| SEP 23 70 | MAR 2 0 1984 | |
| AUG 2 9 1972 | OCT 2 3 1984 | |
| FEB 4 1975 | OCT 21 1985 | |
| JUL 2 9 1975 | MAY 2 3 1986 | |
| MAR 2 3 1977 | AUG 1 1988 | |
| MAR 3 1978 | MAY 1 1989 | |
| MAR 2 0 1978 | MAY 2 9 1989 | |
| FEB 2 3 1979 | AUG 6 1991 | |
| MAR 9 1979 | JAN 26 | |
| MAR 2 3 1979 | | |
| NOV 2 7 1980 | MAR 1 7 JUN 1 1993 | |
| FEB 1 9 1982 | | |
| 3-1-82 | | |
| GAYLORD | | PRINTED IN U.S.A. |